Add and Subtract

$$15 + 6 = \boxed{}$$

Addition tables

Learn the addition tables so you can remember them.

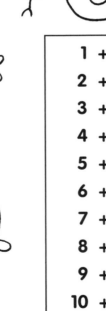

1 + 1 = 2		1 + 2 = 3		
2 + 1 = 3		2 + 2 = 4		
3 + 1 = 4		3 + 2 = 5		
4 + 1 = 5		4 + 2 = 6		
5 + 1 = 6		5 + 2 = 7		
6 + 1 = 7		6 + 2 = 8		
7 + 1 = 8		7 + 2 = 9		
8 + 1 = 9		8 + 2 = 10		
9 + 1 = 10		9 + 2 = 11		
10 + 1 = 11		10 + 2 = 12		
11 + 1 = 12		11 + 2 = 13		
12 + 1 = 13		12 + 2 = 14		

1 + 3 = 4		1 + 4 = 5		
2 + 3 = 5		2 + 4 = 6		
3 + 3 = 6		3 + 4 = 7		
4 + 3 = 7		4 + 4 = 8		
5 + 3 = 8		5 + 4 = 9		
6 + 3 = 9		6 + 4 = 10		
7 + 3 = 10		7 + 4 = 11		
8 + 3 = 11		8 + 4 = 12		
9 + 3 = 12		9 + 4 = 13		
10 + 3 = 13		10 + 4 = 14		
11 + 3 = 14		11 + 4 = 15		
12 + 3 = 15		12 + 4 = 16		

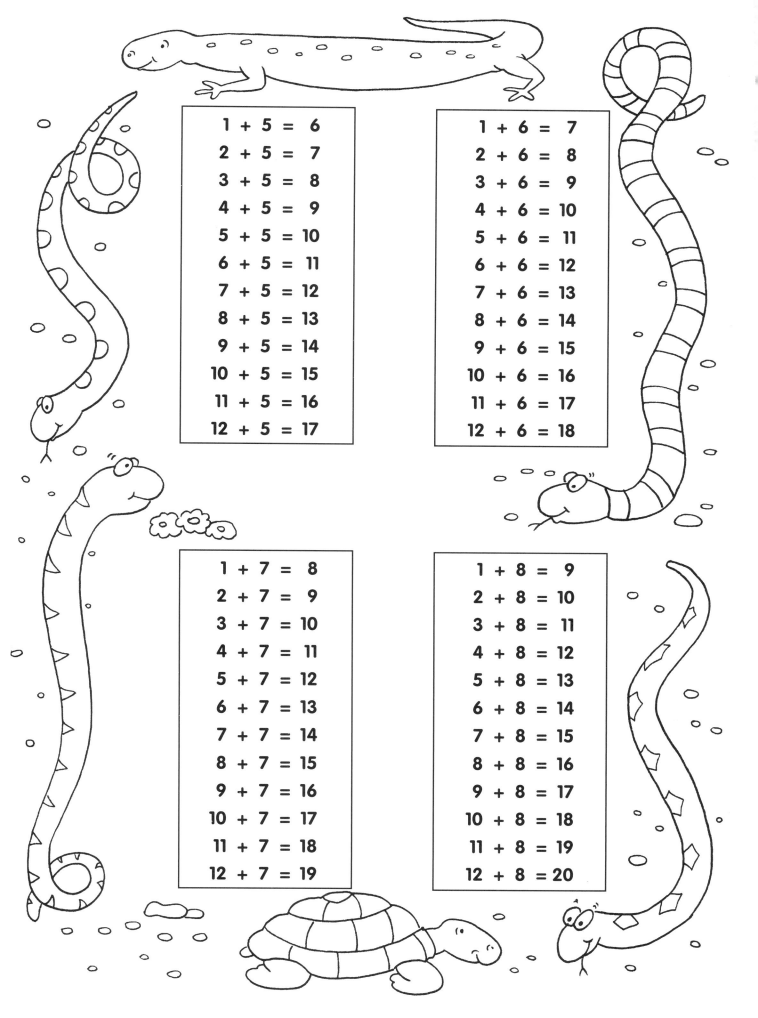

1 + 5 = 6		1 + 6 = 7
2 + 5 = 7		2 + 6 = 8
3 + 5 = 8		3 + 6 = 9
4 + 5 = 9		4 + 6 = 10
5 + 5 = 10		5 + 6 = 11
6 + 5 = 11		6 + 6 = 12
7 + 5 = 12		7 + 6 = 13
8 + 5 = 13		8 + 6 = 14
9 + 5 = 14		9 + 6 = 15
10 + 5 = 15		10 + 6 = 16
11 + 5 = 16		11 + 6 = 17
12 + 5 = 17		12 + 6 = 18

1 + 7 = 8		1 + 8 = 9
2 + 7 = 9		2 + 8 = 10
3 + 7 = 10		3 + 8 = 11
4 + 7 = 11		4 + 8 = 12
5 + 7 = 12		5 + 8 = 13
6 + 7 = 13		6 + 8 = 14
7 + 7 = 14		7 + 8 = 15
8 + 7 = 15		8 + 8 = 16
9 + 7 = 16		9 + 8 = 17
10 + 7 = 17		10 + 8 = 18
11 + 7 = 18		11 + 8 = 19
12 + 7 = 19		12 + 8 = 20

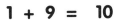

1 + 9 =	10
2 + 9 =	11
3 + 9 =	12
4 + 9 =	13
5 + 9 =	14
6 + 9 =	15
7 + 9 =	16
8 + 9 =	17
9 + 9 =	18
10 + 9 =	19
11 + 9 =	20
12 + 9 =	21

1 + 10 =	11
2 + 10 =	12
3 + 10 =	13
4 + 10 =	14
5 + 10 =	15
6 + 10 =	16
7 + 10 =	17
8 + 10 =	18
9 + 10 =	19
10 + 10 =	20
11 + 10 =	21
12 + 10 =	22

1 + 11 =	12
2 + 11 =	13
3 + 11 =	14
4 + 11 =	15
5 + 11 =	16
6 + 11 =	17
7 + 11 =	18
8 + 11 =	19
9 + 11 =	20
10 + 11 =	21
11 + 11 =	22
12 + 11 =	23

1 + 12 =	13
2 + 12 =	14
3 + 12 =	15
4 + 12 =	16
5 + 12 =	17
6 + 12 =	18
7 + 12 =	19
8 + 12 =	20
9 + 12 =	21
10 + 12 =	22
11 + 12 =	23
12 + 12 =	24

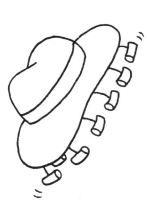

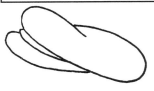

Elephant sums

Do the sums and write the answers in the buckets.

6 + 2 =

4 + 4 =

3 + 7 =

Addition on the farm

Complete the sums.

4 + ☐ = 8

☐ + 7 = 12

7 + ☐ = 14

4 + 3 = ☐

☐ + 6 = 18

9 + ☐ = 16

11 + 5 = ☐

☐ + 8 = 20

8 + 8 = ☐

12 + ☐ = 24

☐ + 8 = 15

10 + 3 = ☐

9 + ☐ = 18

12 + ☐ = 22

11 + 3 = ☐

☐ + 6 = 13

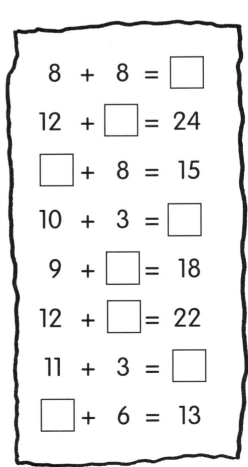

11 + 11 = ☐

7 + ☐ = 19

4 + 3 = ☐

☐ + 11 = 11

8 + ☐ = 21

20 + 3 = ☐

32 + ☐ = 35

18 + 12 = ☐

12 + 12 = ☐

1 + ☐ = 10

☐ + 10 = 20

7 + 9 = ☐

2 + ☐ = 4

8 + 2 = ☐

9 + 7 = ☐

3 + ☐ = 6

Missing numbers

Count the objects to complete the sums.

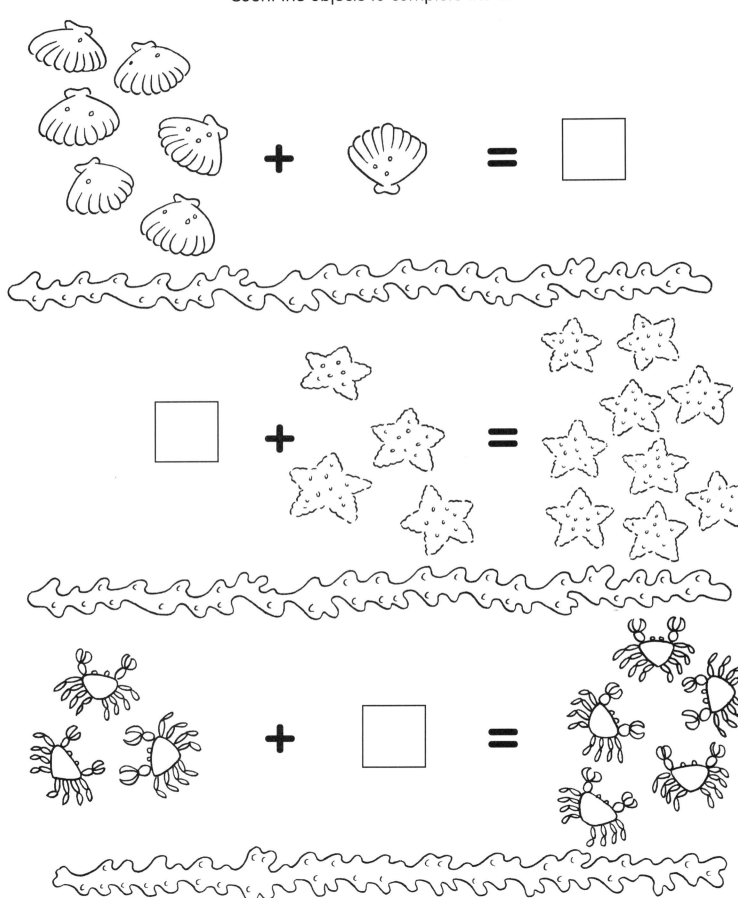

Window sums

Do the sums and write your answers on the doors.

Kite sums

Do the sums by counting the bows on the kites.
When you have an answer, draw the number of bows on the last kite.
The first sum has been started for you.

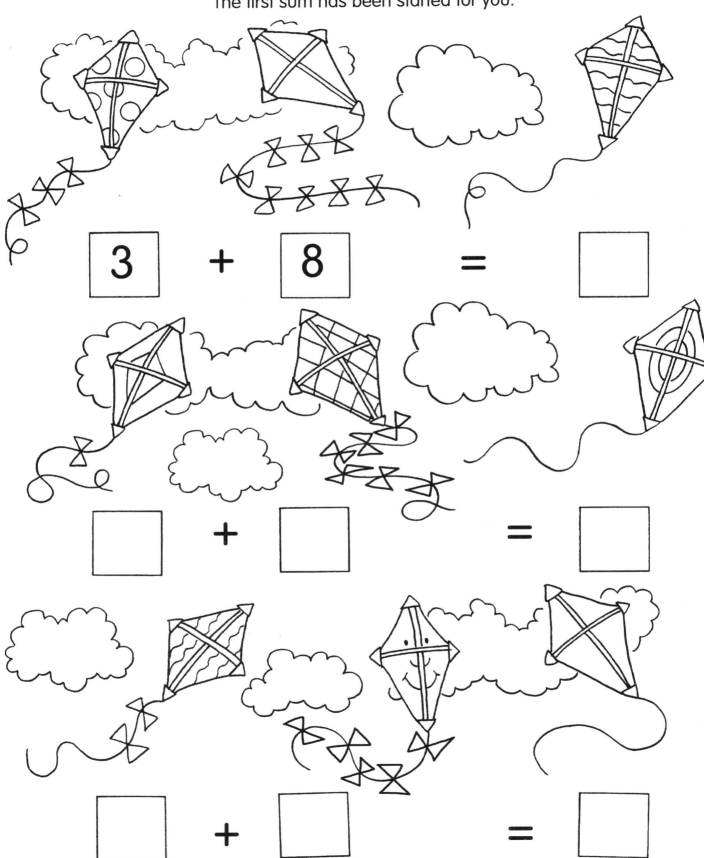

3 + 8 =

☐ + ☐ = ☐

☐ + ☐ = ☐

Balloon sums

The answers to the balloon sums are printed on the children's T-shirts.
Draw a line to join each balloon to the correct child.

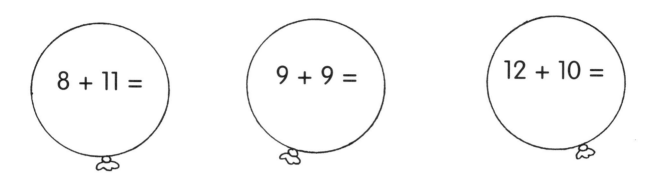

$8 + 11 =$ $9 + 9 =$ $12 + 10 =$

Sums puzzles

Do the sums in the grids by filling in the missing numbers.

	+	8	=	12
+	■	+	■	+
1	+		=	
=	■	=	■	=
	+	11	=	16

11	+		=	20
+	■	+	■	+
	+	2	=	4
=	■	=	■	=
	+	11	=	

Sums crossword

Do the sums. Follow the letters across and down, and write the answers
as words in the crossword grid.

↓ a. 6 + 6 = ☐

a. 2 + 0 = ☐
→

b. 3 + 7 = ☐

c. 9 + 2 = ☐

d. 3 + 1 = ☐

e. 1 + 0 = ☐

f. 2 + 1 = ☐

g. 5 + 3 = ☐

Number lines

Do the sums in the hot-air balloons.
Draw lines to join each answer to its place on the number line.

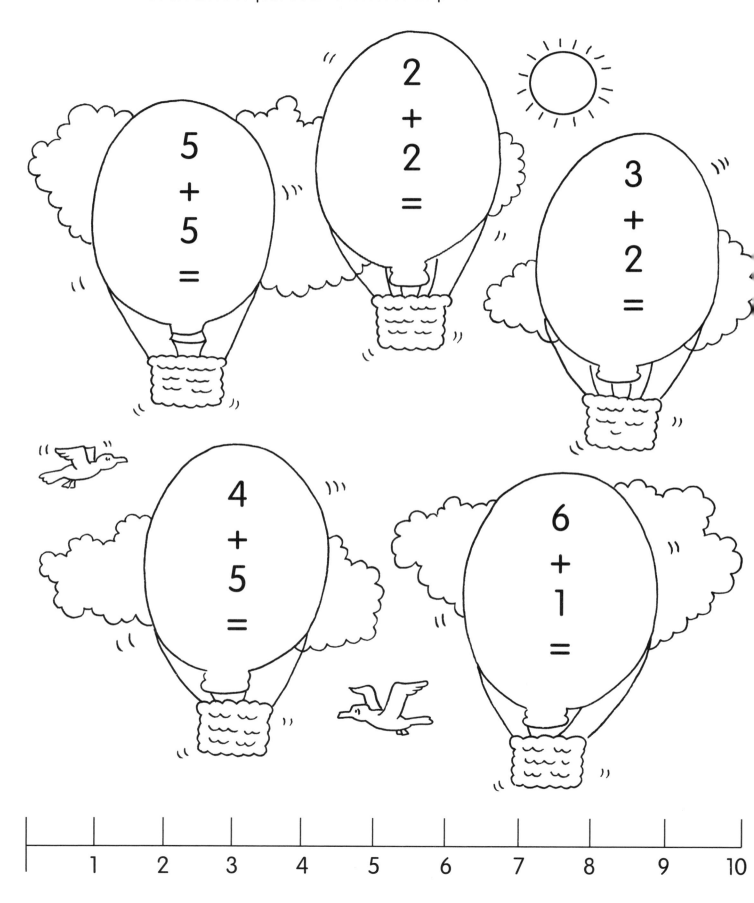

Match the answers

Draw lines to join the sums on the sailboats to their answers on the anchors.

Addition test

Do the sums and write the answers in the boxes.
Check your answers by looking at the tables.

11 + 2 =

6 + 7 =

10 + 5 =

6 + 9 =

3 + 12 =

2 + 8 =

7 + 6 =

5 + 5 =

8 + 8 =

10 + 3 =

2 + 2 =

4 + 5 =

5 + 8 =

1 + 9 =

3 + 3 =

6 + 6 =

4 + 7 =

9 + 6 =

11 + 11 =

7 + 12 =

3 + 9 =

4 + 2 =

12 + 4 =

8 + 4 =

10 + 6 =

5 + 3 =

Subtraction tables

Learn the subtraction tables so you can remember them.

2	-	1	=	1	3	-	2	=	1
3	-	1	=	2	4	-	2	=	2
4	-	1	=	3	5	-	2	=	3
5	-	1	=	4	6	-	2	=	4
6	-	1	=	5	7	-	2	=	5
7	-	1	=	6	8	-	2	=	6
8	-	1	=	7	9	-	2	=	7
9	-	1	=	8	10	-	2	=	8
10	-	1	=	9	11	-	2	=	9
11	-	1	=	10	12	-	2	=	10
12	-	1	=	11	13	-	2	=	11
13	-	1	=	12	14	-	2	=	12

4	-	3	=	1	5	-	4	=	1
5	-	3	=	2	6	-	4	=	2
6	-	3	=	3	7	-	4	=	3
7	-	3	=	4	8	-	4	=	4
8	-	3	=	5	9	-	4	=	5
9	-	3	=	6	10	-	4	=	6
10	-	3	=	7	11	-	4	=	7
11	-	3	=	8	12	-	4	=	8
12	-	3	=	9	13	-	4	=	9
13	-	3	=	10	14	-	4	=	10
14	-	3	=	11	15	-	4	=	11
15	-	3	=	12	16	-	4	=	12

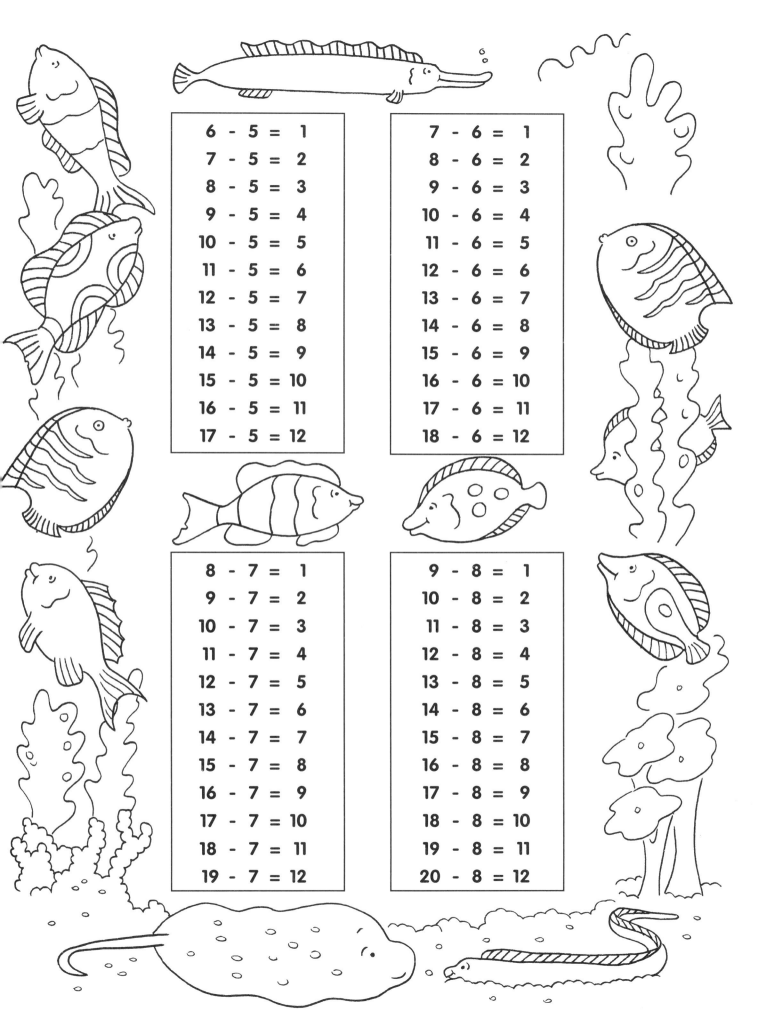

6	-	5	=	1
7	-	5	=	2
8	-	5	=	3
9	-	5	=	4
10	-	5	=	5
11	-	5	=	6
12	-	5	=	7
13	-	5	=	8
14	-	5	=	9
15	-	5	=	10
16	-	5	=	11
17	-	5	=	12

6 - 5 = 1
7 - 5 = 2
8 - 5 = 3
9 - 5 = 4
10 - 5 = 5
11 - 5 = 6
12 - 5 = 7
13 - 5 = 8
14 - 5 = 9
15 - 5 = 10
16 - 5 = 11
17 - 5 = 12

7 - 6 = 1
8 - 6 = 2
9 - 6 = 3
10 - 6 = 4
11 - 6 = 5
12 - 6 = 6
13 - 6 = 7
14 - 6 = 8
15 - 6 = 9
16 - 6 = 10
17 - 6 = 11
18 - 6 = 12

8 - 7 = 1
9 - 7 = 2
10 - 7 = 3
11 - 7 = 4
12 - 7 = 5
13 - 7 = 6
14 - 7 = 7
15 - 7 = 8
16 - 7 = 9
17 - 7 = 10
18 - 7 = 11
19 - 7 = 12

9 - 8 = 1
10 - 8 = 2
11 - 8 = 3
12 - 8 = 4
13 - 8 = 5
14 - 8 = 6
15 - 8 = 7
16 - 8 = 8
17 - 8 = 9
18 - 8 = 10
19 - 8 = 11
20 - 8 = 12

10	- 9 =	1
11	- 9 =	2
12	- 9 =	3
13	- 9 =	4
14	- 9 =	5
15	- 9 =	6
16	- 9 =	7
17	- 9 =	8
18	- 9 =	9
19	- 9 =	10
20	- 9 =	11
21	- 9 =	12

11 - 10 =	1
12 - 10 =	2
13 - 10 =	3
14 - 10 =	4
15 - 10 =	5
16 - 10 =	6
17 - 10 =	7
18 - 10 =	8
19 - 10 =	9
20 - 10 =	10
21 - 10 =	11
22 - 10 =	12

12 - 11 =	1
13 - 11 =	2
14 - 11 =	3
15 - 11 =	4
16 - 11 =	5
17 - 11 =	6
18 - 11 =	7
19 - 11 =	8
20 - 11 =	9
21 - 11 =	10
22 - 11 =	11
23 - 11 =	12

13 - 12 =	1
14 - 12 =	2
15 - 12 =	3
16 - 12 =	4
17 - 12 =	5
18 - 12 =	6
19 - 12 =	7
20 - 12 =	8
21 - 12 =	9
22 - 12 =	10
23 - 12 =	11
24 - 12 =	12

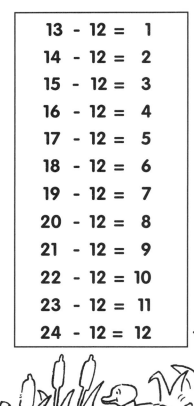

Penguin sums

Do the sums.

6 − 2 =

12 − 10 =

20 − 9 =

Subtraction in space

Complete the sums.

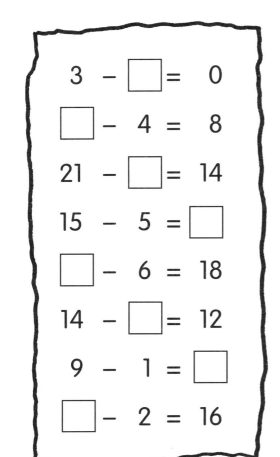

3 – ☐ = 0

☐ – 4 = 8

21 – ☐ = 14

15 – 5 = ☐

☐ – 6 = 18

14 – ☐ = 12

9 – 1 = ☐

☐ – 2 = 16

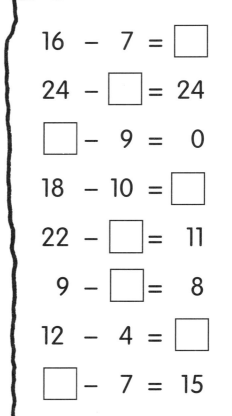

16 – 7 = ☐

24 – ☐ = 24

☐ – 9 = 0

18 – 10 = ☐

22 – ☐ = 11

9 – ☐ = 8

12 – 4 = ☐

☐ – 7 = 15

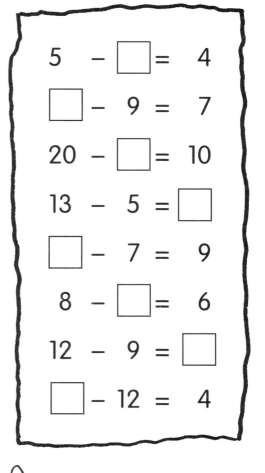

5 − ☐ = 4

☐ − 9 = 7

20 − ☐ = 10

13 − 5 = ☐

☐ − 7 = 9

8 − ☐ = 6

12 − 9 = ☐

☐ − 12 = 4

12 − 12 = ☐

10 − ☐ = 5

☐ − 10 = 2

15 − 9 = ☐

18 − ☐ = 17

20 − ☐ = 16

15 − 3 = ☐

☐ − 1 = 5

Bubble sums

Working upwards from the bubbles at the bottom, do the sums
by filling in the missing numbers.

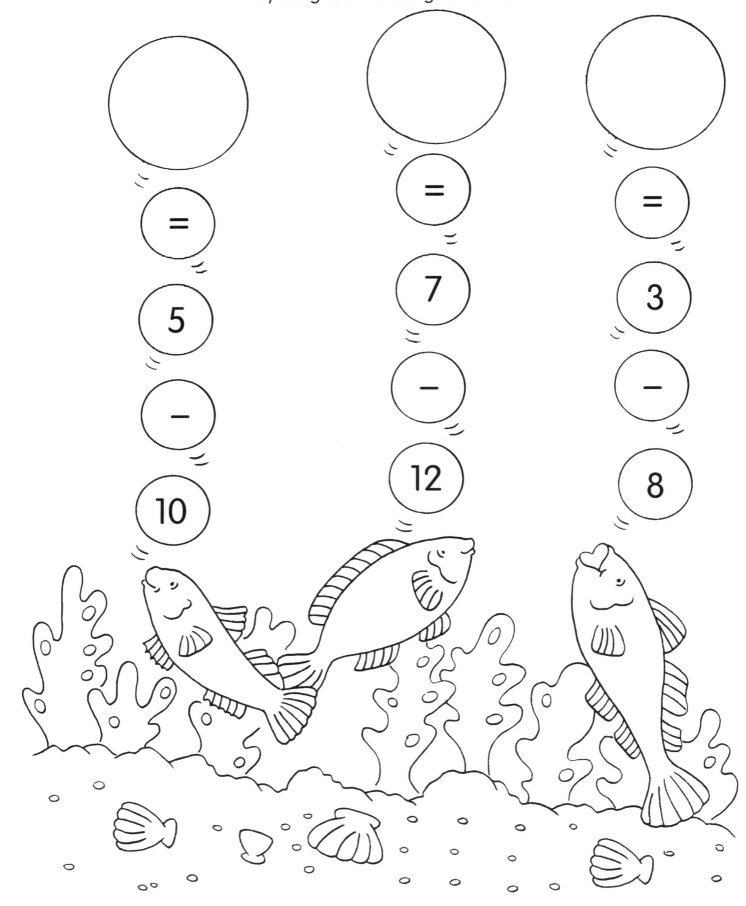

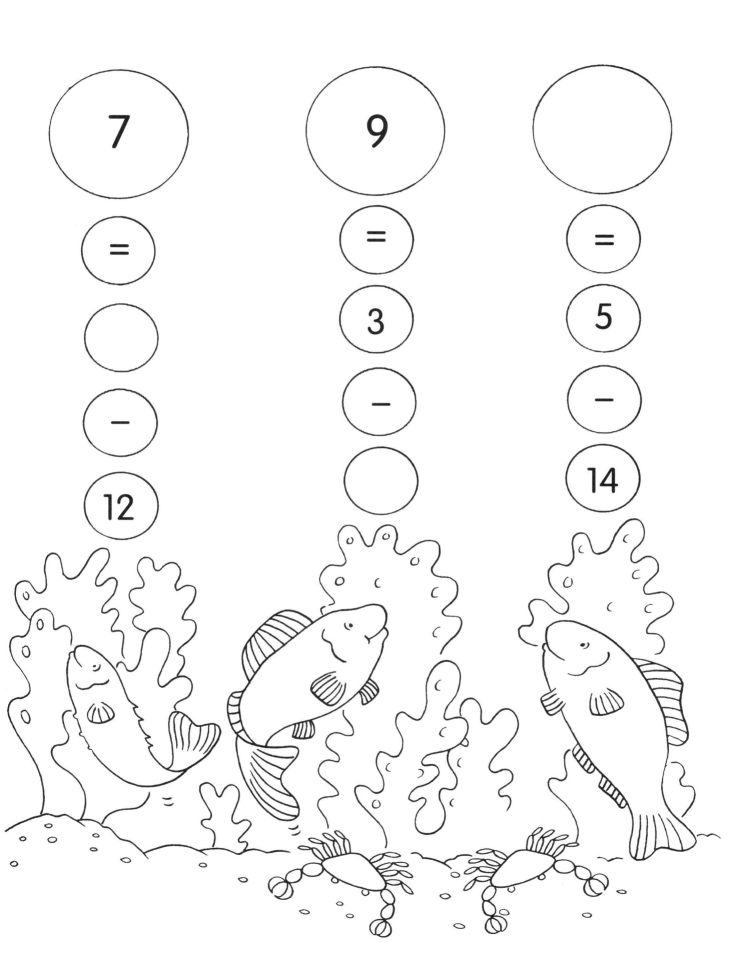

Fun with sums

Solve these problems.

Take 4 bananas away from these monkeys.
How many bananas are left?

If 3 parrots fly away, how many parrots are left?

Colour 6 of the crocodile's teeth. How many teeth are left white?

Two rabbits eat 2 carrots each.
How many carrots are left?

Draw 8 lighted candles on this cake.
If the boy blows out 3 candles,
how many lighted candles are left?

Which is right?

Circle the sums with answers that match
the numbers at the top of each box.

18
10 – 7
33 – 12
15 – 3
27 – 9

40
25 – 5
50 – 10
48 – 6
10 – 5

24
30 – 6
42 – 7
64 – 8
20 – 2

21
45 – 5
21 – 7
30 – 9
10 – 4

10
5 – 5
10 – 1
12 – 2
18 – 7

8
88 – 10
16 – 8
12 – 6
72 – 9

Taking away wordsearch

Do the sums and write the answers in the boxes.
Look for the written answers in the wordsearch grid.
You will find them by reading across and down.
Draw a ring around the words as you find them.

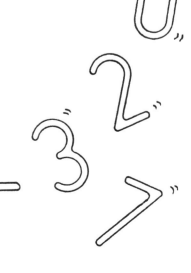

10 − 3 = ☐	15 − 9 = ☐
6 − 2 = ☐	20 − 10 = ☐
12 − 7 = ☐	50 − 20 = ☐
3 − 2 = ☐	8 − 6 = ☐

I	E	R	F	O	R	T	B	N
X	K	S	P	S	O	H	J	H
A	S	E	P	C	D	I	V	G
F	I	V	E	Y	T	R	E	X
B	N	E	W	E	R	T	E	N
H	B	N	E	M	K	Y	O	P
T	I	J	F	Y	A	G	S	X
W	D	F	O	N	E	B	I	J
O	Y	T	U	E	X	R	X	N
M	A	I	R	B	F	G	R	E

Subtraction test

Do the sums and write the answers in the boxes.
Check your answers by looking at the tables.

8   –   4 = ☐

12   –   2 = ☐

17   –   5 = ☐

20   –   9 = ☐

9   –   1 = ☐

13   –   5 = ☐

24   –   12 = ☐

5   –   5 = ☐

11   –   3 = ☐

20   –   12 = ☐

10   –   4 = ☐

23   –   11 = ☐

13 − 8 =

11 − 1 =

15 − 9 =

3 − 3 =

18 − 6 =

7 − 2 =

16 − 6 =

15 − 5 =

17 − 3 =

7 − 3 =

14 − 12 =

17 − 8 =

6 − 5 =

22 − 10 =

Answers

Elephant sums
6 + 2 = 8   4 + 4 = 8   3 + 7 = 10

Addition on the farm
4 + 4 = 8   8 + 8 = 16
5 + 7 = 12   12 + 12 = 24
7 + 7 = 14   7 + 8 = 15
4 + 3 = 7   10 + 3 = 13
12 + 6 = 18   9 + 9 = 18
9 + 7 = 16   12 + 10 = 22
11 + 5 = 16   11 + 3 = 14
12 + 8 = 20   7 + 6 = 13

11 + 11 = 22   12 + 12 = 24
7 + 12 = 19   1 + 9 = 10
4 + 3 = 7   10 + 10 = 20
0 + 11 = 11   7 + 9 = 16
8 + 13 = 21   2 + 2 = 4
20 + 3 = 23   8 + 2 = 10
32 + 3 = 35   9 + 7 = 16
18 + 12 = 30   3 + 3 = 6

Missing numbers
6 + 1 = 7   5 + 4 = 9   3 + 2 = 5

Window sums
3 + 12 = 15   5 + 5 = 10   9 + 6 = 15

Kite sums
3 + 8 = 11   1 + 6 = 7   2 + 5 = 7

Balloon sums
8 + 11 = 19   9 + 9 = 18   12 + 10 = 22

Sums puzzles

4	+	8	=	12
+	■	+	■	+
1	+	3	=	4
=	■	=	■	=
5	+	11	=	16

11	+	9	=	20
+	■	+	■	+
2	+	2	=	4
=	■	=	■	=
13	+	11	=	24

Sums crossword
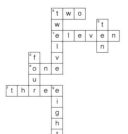

Number lines
5 + 5 = 10   2 + 2 = 4   3 + 2 = 5
4 + 5 = 9   6 + 1 = 7

Match the answers
7 + 7 = 14   8 + 8 = 16
11 + 11 = 22   10 + 10 = 20

Penguin sums
6 - 2 = 4   12 - 10 = 2   20 - 9 = 11

Subtractions in space
3 – 3 = 0   16 – 7 = 9
12 – 4 = 8   24 – 0 = 24
21 – 7 = 14   9 – 9 = 0
15 – 5 = 10   18 – 10 = 8
24 – 6 = 18   22 – 11 = 11
14 – 2 = 12   9 – 1 = 8
9 – 1 = 8   12 – 4 = 8
18 – 2 = 16   22 – 7 = 15

5 – 1 = 4   12 – 12 = 0
16 – 9 = 7   10 – 5 = 5
20 – 10 = 10   12 – 10 = 2
13 – 5 = 8   15 – 9 = 6
16 – 7 = 9   18 – 1 = 17
8 – 2 = 6   20 – 4 = 16
12 – 9 = 3   15 – 3 = 12
16 – 12 = 4   6 – 1 = 5

Bubble sums
10 - 5 = 5   12 - 7 = 5   8 - 3 = 5
12 - 5 = 7   12 - 3 = 9   14 - 5 = 9

Fun with sums
2 bananas are left   2 carrots are left
4 parrots are left   5 candles are left
5 teeth are left white

Which is right?
27 - 9 = 18   50 - 10 = 40   30 - 6 = 24
30 - 9 = 21   12 - 2 = 10   16 - 8 = 16

Taking away wordsearch

Multiply and Divide

$$9 \times 7 =$$

Multiplication tables

Learn the multiplication tables so you can remember them.

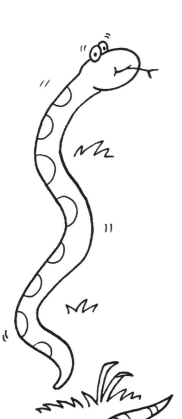

1 x 1 = 1	1 x 2 = 2
2 x 1 = 2	2 x 2 = 4
3 x 1 = 3	3 x 2 = 6
4 x 1 = 4	4 x 2 = 8
5 x 1 = 5	5 x 2 = 10
6 x 1 = 6	6 x 2 = 12
7 x 1 = 7	7 x 2 = 14
8 x 1 = 8	8 x 2 = 16
9 x 1 = 9	9 x 2 = 18
10 x 1 = 10	10 x 2 = 20
11 x 1 = 11	11 x 2 = 22
12 x 1 = 12	12 x 2 = 24

1 x 3 = 3	1 x 4 = 4
2 x 3 = 6	2 x 4 = 8
3 x 3 = 9	3 x 4 = 12
4 x 3 = 12	4 x 4 = 16
5 x 3 = 15	5 x 4 = 20
6 x 3 = 18	6 x 4 = 24
7 x 3 = 21	7 x 4 = 28
8 x 3 = 24	8 x 4 = 32
9 x 3 = 27	9 x 4 = 36
10 x 3 = 30	10 x 4 = 40
11 x 3 = 33	11 x 4 = 44
12 x 3 = 36	12 x 4 = 48

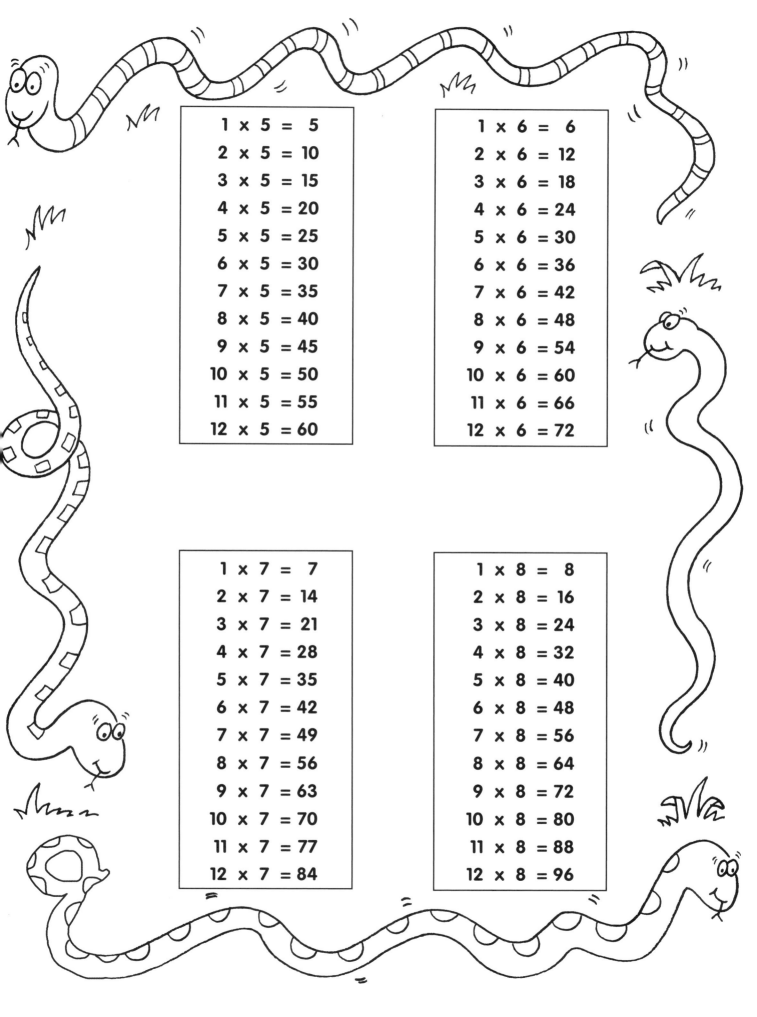

1	x 5	=	5
2	x 5	=	10
3	x 5	=	15
4	x 5	=	20
5	x 5	=	25
6	x 5	=	30
7	x 5	=	35
8	x 5	=	40
9	x 5	=	45
10	x 5	=	50
11	x 5	=	55
12	x 5	=	60

1	x 6	=	6
2	x 6	=	12
3	x 6	=	18
4	x 6	=	24
5	x 6	=	30
6	x 6	=	36
7	x 6	=	42
8	x 6	=	48
9	x 6	=	54
10	x 6	=	60
11	x 6	=	66
12	x 6	=	72

1	x 7	=	7
2	x 7	=	14
3	x 7	=	21
4	x 7	=	28
5	x 7	=	35
6	x 7	=	42
7	x 7	=	49
8	x 7	=	56
9	x 7	=	63
10	x 7	=	70
11	x 7	=	77
12	x 7	=	84

1	x 8	=	8
2	x 8	=	16
3	x 8	=	24
4	x 8	=	32
5	x 8	=	40
6	x 8	=	48
7	x 8	=	56
8	x 8	=	64
9	x 8	=	72
10	x 8	=	80
11	x 8	=	88
12	x 8	=	96

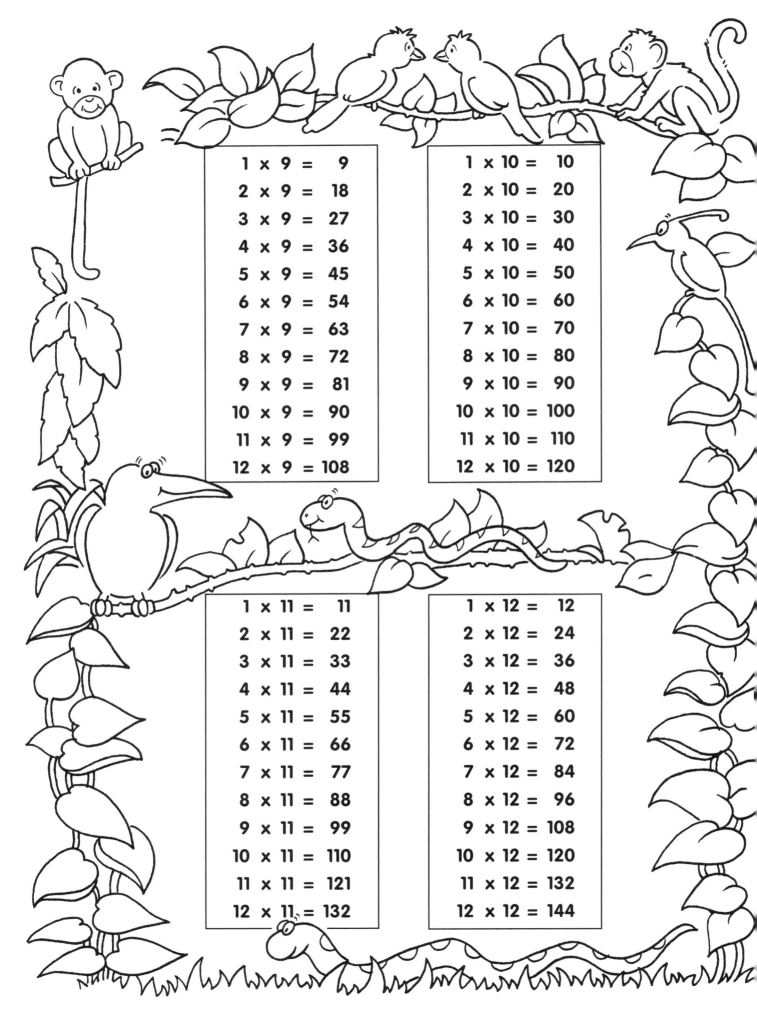

1 × 9 =	9	
2 × 9 =	18	
3 × 9 =	27	
4 × 9 =	36	
5 × 9 =	45	
6 × 9 =	54	
7 × 9 =	63	
8 × 9 =	72	
9 × 9 =	81	
10 × 9 =	90	
11 × 9 =	99	
12 × 9 =	108	

1 × 10 =	10
2 × 10 =	20
3 × 10 =	30
4 × 10 =	40
5 × 10 =	50
6 × 10 =	60
7 × 10 =	70
8 × 10 =	80
9 × 10 =	90
10 × 10 =	100
11 × 10 =	110
12 × 10 =	120

1 × 11 =	11
2 × 11 =	22
3 × 11 =	33
4 × 11 =	44
5 × 11 =	55
6 × 11 =	66
7 × 11 =	77
8 × 11 =	88
9 × 11 =	99
10 × 11 =	110
11 × 11 =	121
12 × 11 =	132

1 × 12 =	12
2 × 12 =	24
3 × 12 =	36
4 × 12 =	48
5 × 12 =	60
6 × 12 =	72
7 × 12 =	84
8 × 12 =	96
9 × 12 =	108
10 × 12 =	120
11 × 12 =	132
12 × 12 =	144

Multiplication sums

Do the sums and write the answers on the rocks.

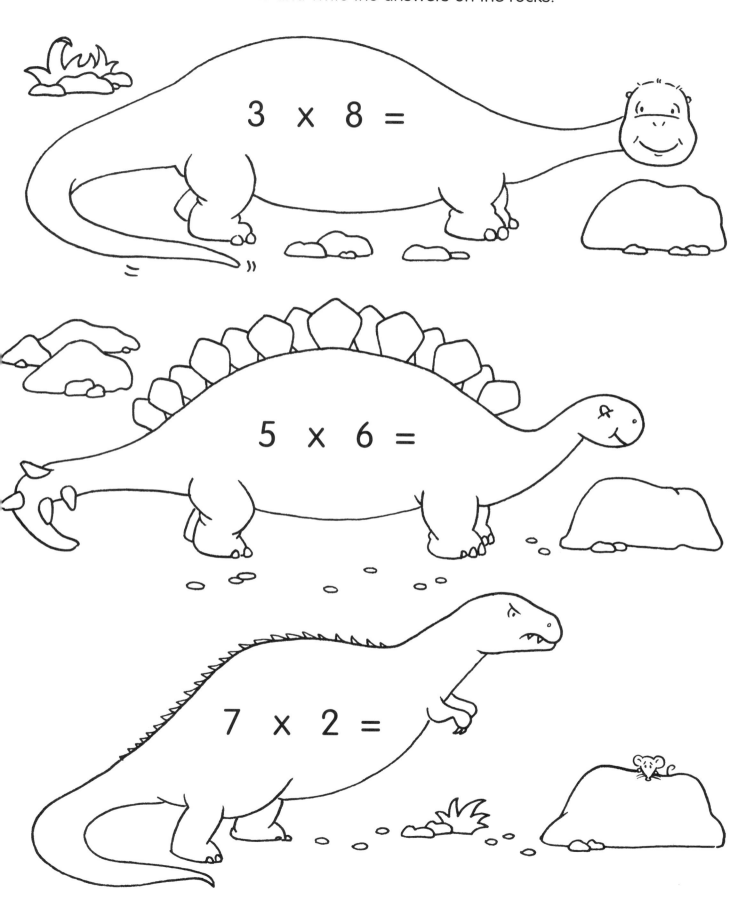

3 x 8 =

5 x 6 =

7 x 2 =

Missing numbers

Complete the multiplication sums.

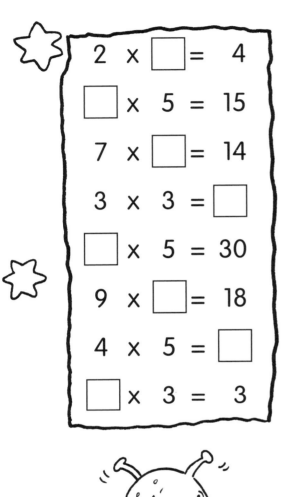

2 x ☐ = 4

☐ x 5 = 15

7 x ☐ = 14

3 x 3 = ☐

☐ x 5 = 30

9 x ☐ = 18

4 x 5 = ☐

☐ x 3 = 3

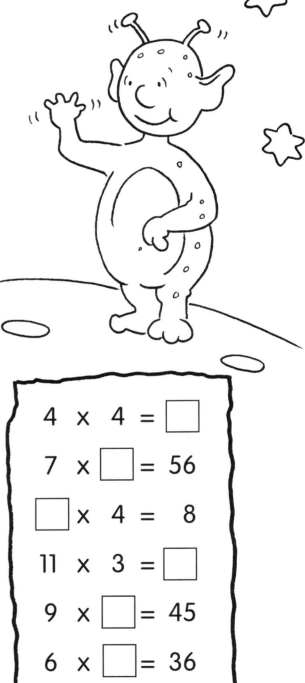

4 x 4 = ☐

7 x ☐ = 56

☐ x 4 = 8

11 x 3 = ☐

9 x ☐ = 45

6 x ☐ = 36

8 x 3 = ☐

☐ x 7 = 28

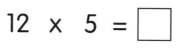

12 × 5 = ☐

10 × ☐ = 30

4 × 3 = ☐

☐ × 11 = 11

8 × ☐ = 40

9 × 3 = ☐

8 × ☐ = 72

12 × 12 = ☐

11 × 10 = ☐

6 × ☐ = 48

☐ × 4 = 24

7 × 9 = ☐

2 × ☐ = 4

12 × 8 = ☐

9 × 9 = ☐

3 × ☐ = 21

Missing bees

Draw more bees to complete the sums.

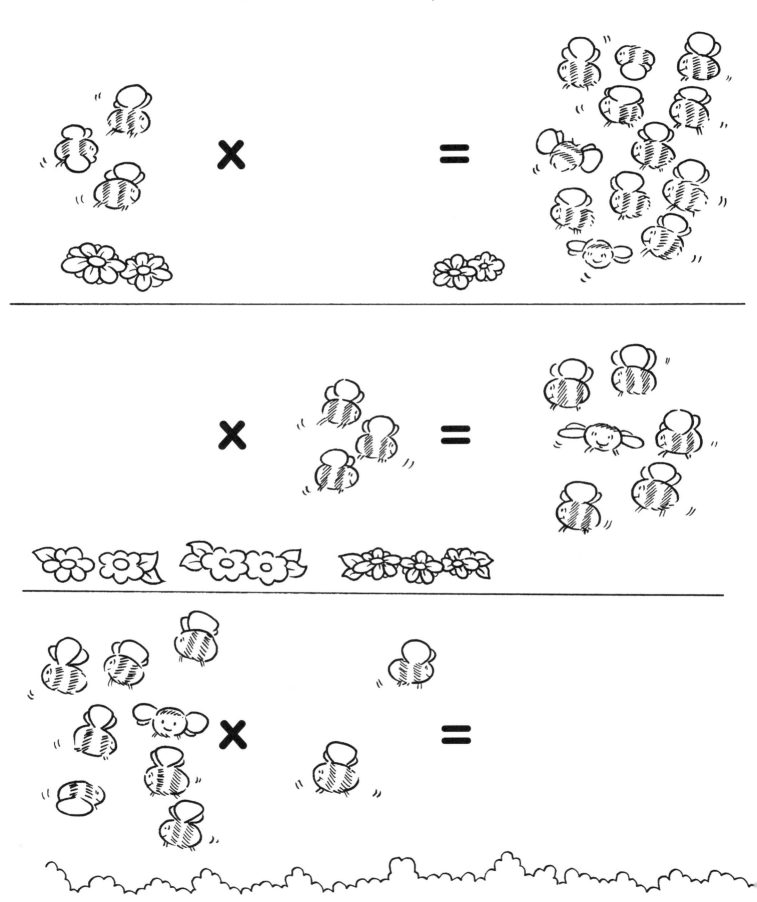

Sum ladders

Do the sums in the ladders and write the answers on the buckets.

Flower sums

Count the petals and write the number in the centre of each flower.
Then do the sums. You could draw the missing petals on the last flower in each row.
Look at the example to help you.

Example:

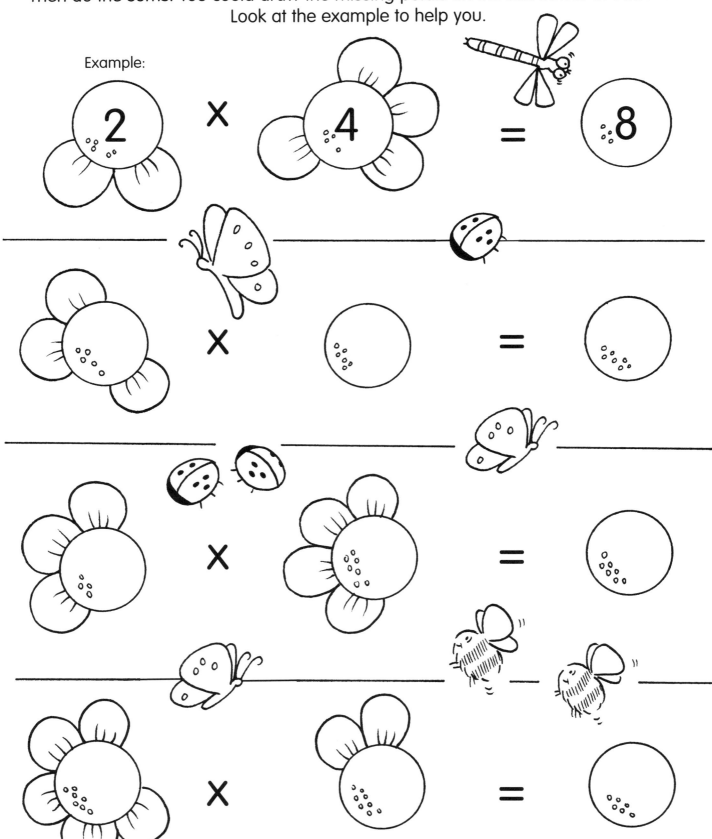

Magical numbers

The children are holding the answers to the sums on the cooking pots.
Draw a line to join each child to the correct pot.

24   90   9

3 x 3

4 x 6

10 x 9

Sums puzzles

Do the sums in the grids by filling in the missing numbers.

Sums crossword

Do the sums. Following the letters across and down, write the answers
as words in the crossword grid.

a.	$3 \times 4 =$	☐
b.	$2 \times 1 =$	☐
→c.	$2 \times 7 =$	☐
↓c.	$5 \times 10 =$	☐

d.	$3 \times 3 =$	☐
e.	$1 \times 11 =$	☐
f.	$7 \times 10 =$	☐
g.	$10 \times 1 =$	☐

Match the answers

Do the sums on the spaceships. Look at the answers then draw
a line to join the correct aliens to the spaceships.

Multiplication test

Do the sums and write the answers in the boxes.
Check your answers by looking at the tables.

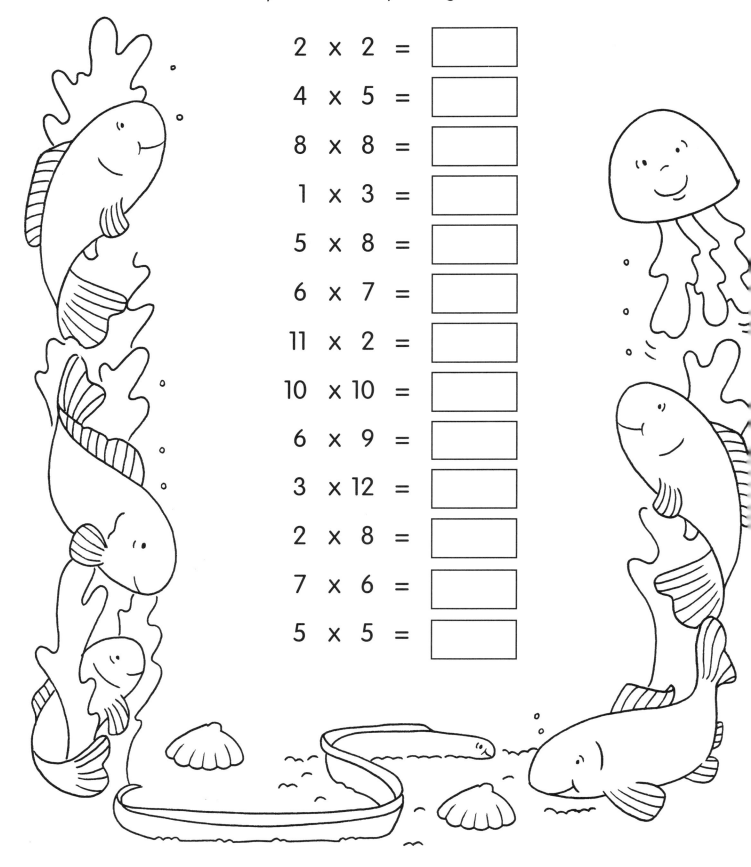

2 x 2 = ☐

4 x 5 = ☐

8 x 8 = ☐

1 x 3 = ☐

5 x 8 = ☐

6 x 7 = ☐

11 x 2 = ☐

10 x 10 = ☐

6 x 9 = ☐

3 x 12 = ☐

2 x 8 = ☐

7 x 6 = ☐

5 x 5 = ☐

7 × 12 = ☐

3 × 9 = ☐

4 × 4 = ☐

5 × 4 = ☐

4 × 7 = ☐

9 × 6 = ☐

11 × 11 = ☐

8 × 4 = ☐

12 × 6 = ☐

1 × 9 = ☐

3 × 3 = ☐

6 × 6 = ☐

8 × 3 = ☐

Division tables

Learn the division tables so you can remember them.

1 ÷ 1 = 1		2 ÷ 2 = 1
2 ÷ 1 = 2		4 ÷ 2 = 2
3 ÷ 1 = 3		6 ÷ 2 = 3
4 ÷ 1 = 4		8 ÷ 2 = 4
5 ÷ 1 = 5		10 ÷ 2 = 5
6 ÷ 1 = 6		12 ÷ 2 = 6
7 ÷ 1 = 7		14 ÷ 2 = 7
8 ÷ 1 = 8		16 ÷ 2 = 8
9 ÷ 1 = 9		18 ÷ 2 = 9
10 ÷ 1 = 10		20 ÷ 2 = 10
11 ÷ 1 = 11		22 ÷ 2 = 11
12 ÷ 1 = 12		24 ÷ 2 = 12

3 ÷ 3 = 1		4 ÷ 4 = 1
6 ÷ 3 = 2		8 ÷ 4 = 2
9 ÷ 3 = 3		12 ÷ 4 = 3
12 ÷ 3 = 4		16 ÷ 4 = 4
15 ÷ 3 = 5		20 ÷ 4 = 5
18 ÷ 3 = 6		24 ÷ 4 = 6
21 ÷ 3 = 7		28 ÷ 4 = 7
24 ÷ 3 = 8		32 ÷ 4 = 8
27 ÷ 3 = 9		36 ÷ 4 = 9
30 ÷ 3 = 10		40 ÷ 4 = 10
33 ÷ 3 = 11		44 ÷ 4 = 11
36 ÷ 3 = 12		48 ÷ 4 = 12

| 5 ÷ 5 = 1 |
| 10 ÷ 5 = 2 |
| 15 ÷ 5 = 3 |
| 20 ÷ 5 = 4 |
| 25 ÷ 5 = 5 |
| 30 ÷ 5 = 6 |
| 35 ÷ 5 = 7 |
| 40 ÷ 5 = 8 |
| 45 ÷ 5 = 9 |
| 50 ÷ 5 = 10 |
| 55 ÷ 5 = 11 |
| 60 ÷ 5 = 12 |

| 6 ÷ 6 = 1 |
| 12 ÷ 6 = 2 |
| 18 ÷ 6 = 3 |
| 24 ÷ 6 = 4 |
| 30 ÷ 6 = 5 |
| 36 ÷ 6 = 6 |
| 42 ÷ 6 = 7 |
| 48 ÷ 6 = 8 |
| 54 ÷ 6 = 9 |
| 60 ÷ 6 = 10 |
| 66 ÷ 6 = 11 |
| 72 ÷ 6 = 12 |

| 7 ÷ 7 = 1 |
| 14 ÷ 7 = 2 |
| 21 ÷ 7 = 3 |
| 28 ÷ 7 = 4 |
| 35 ÷ 7 = 5 |
| 42 ÷ 7 = 6 |
| 49 ÷ 7 = 7 |
| 56 ÷ 7 = 8 |
| 63 ÷ 7 = 9 |
| 70 ÷ 7 = 10 |
| 77 ÷ 7 = 11 |
| 84 ÷ 7 = 12 |

| 8 ÷ 8 = 1 |
| 16 ÷ 8 = 2 |
| 24 ÷ 8 = 3 |
| 32 ÷ 8 = 4 |
| 40 ÷ 8 = 5 |
| 48 ÷ 8 = 6 |
| 56 ÷ 8 = 7 |
| 64 ÷ 8 = 8 |
| 72 ÷ 8 = 9 |
| 80 ÷ 8 = 10 |
| 88 ÷ 8 = 11 |
| 96 ÷ 8 = 12 |

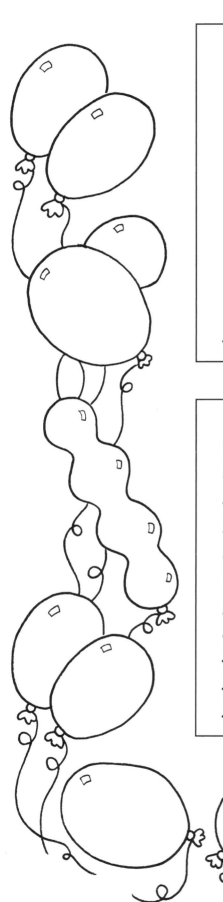

9 ÷ 9	=	1
18 ÷ 9	=	2
27 ÷ 9	=	3
36 ÷ 9	=	4
45 ÷ 9	=	5
54 ÷ 9	=	6
63 ÷ 9	=	7
72 ÷ 9	=	8
81 ÷ 9	=	9
90 ÷ 9	=	10
99 ÷ 9	=	11
108 ÷ 9	=	12

10 ÷ 10	=	1
20 ÷ 10	=	2
30 ÷ 10	=	3
40 ÷ 10	=	4
50 ÷ 10	=	5
60 ÷ 10	=	6
70 ÷ 10	=	7
80 ÷ 10	=	8
90 ÷ 10	=	9
100 ÷ 10	=	10
110 ÷ 10	=	11
120 ÷ 10	=	12

11 ÷ 11	=	1
22 ÷ 11	=	2
33 ÷ 11	=	3
44 ÷ 11	=	4
55 ÷ 11	=	5
66 ÷ 11	=	6
77 ÷ 11	=	7
88 ÷ 11	=	8
99 ÷ 11	=	9
110 ÷ 11	=	10
121 ÷ 11	=	11
132 ÷ 11	=	12

12 ÷ 12	=	1
24 ÷ 12	=	2
36 ÷ 12	=	3
48 ÷ 12	=	4
60 ÷ 12	=	5
72 ÷ 12	=	6
84 ÷ 12	=	7
96 ÷ 12	=	8
108 ÷ 12	=	9
120 ÷ 12	=	10
132 ÷ 12	=	11
144 ÷ 12	=	12

Butterfly sums

Draw more butterflies to complete the sums.

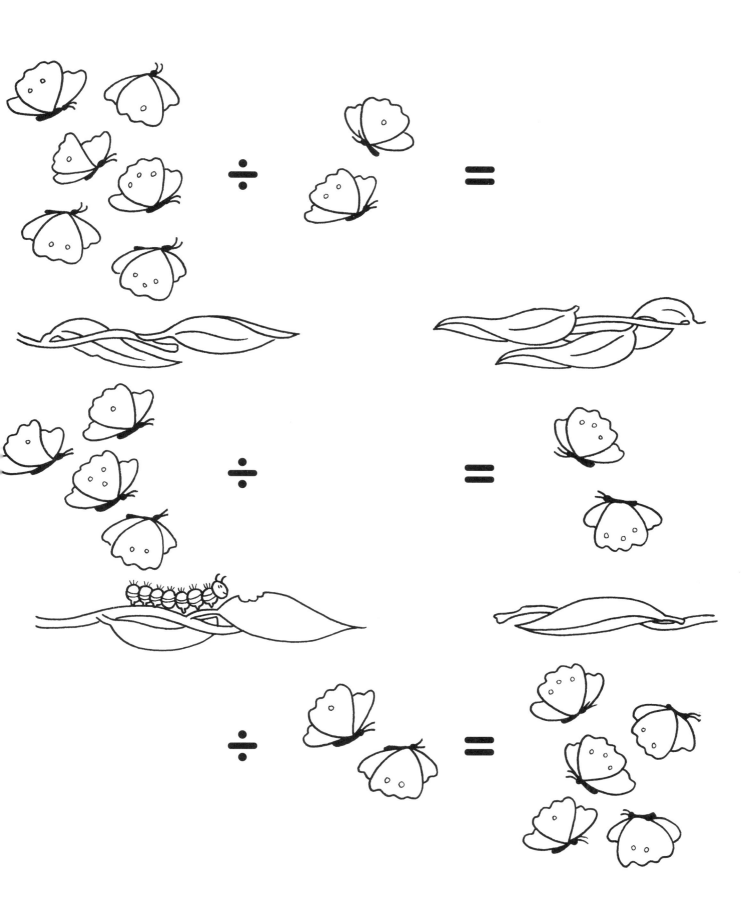

Missing numbers

Complete the sums.

4 ÷ ☐ = 1

☐ ÷ 4 = 2

21 ÷ ☐ = 3

54 ÷ 6 = ☐

☐ ÷ 6 = 6

63 ÷ ☐ = 7

49 ÷ 7 = ☐

☐ ÷ 9 = 11

12 ÷ 6 = ☐

36 ÷ ☐ = 4

☐ ÷ 9 = 1

56 ÷ 7 = ☐

42 ÷ ☐ = 6

18 ÷ ☐ = 3

20 ÷ 4 = ☐

☐ ÷ 7 = 4

$$24 \div \boxed{} = 4$$

$$\boxed{} \div 9 = 2$$

$$70 \div \boxed{} = 10$$

$$99 \div 9 = \boxed{}$$

$$\boxed{} \div 6 = 8$$

$$27 \div \boxed{} = 3$$

$$32 \div 4 = \boxed{}$$

$$\boxed{} \div 9 = 5$$

$$30 \div 6 = \boxed{}$$

$$10 \div \boxed{} = 2$$

$$\boxed{} \div 8 = 9$$

$$40 \div 5 = \boxed{}$$

$$90 \div \boxed{} = 9$$

$$56 \div \boxed{} = 7$$

$$6 \div 3 = \boxed{}$$

$$\boxed{} \div 8 = 3$$

Star sums

Do the sums in the stars and write the answers in the boxes.

$81 \div 9$

$35 \div 5$

$49 \div 7$

$12 \div 6$

$3 \div 3$

$20 \div 5$

$32 \div 4$

$55 \div 11$

Juggling sums

Do the sums by filling in the missing numbers.

$6 \div 3 = \square$

$\square \div 2 = 8$

$\square \div 7 = 6$

$24 \div \square = 6$

$27 \div 3 = \square$

$30 \div 5 = \square$

$9 \div \square = 9$

$\square \div 9 = 7$

Solve these problems

Share 16 books equally between 4 children.
How many books each?

Share 7 ice creams equally between 3 children. How many ice creams each?
How many left over?

Share 8 carrots equally between 2 rabbits.
How many carrots each?

Share 14 bananas equally between 7 monkeys.
How many bananas each?

Share 9 buns equally between 2 elephants. How many buns each?
How many left over?

Share 9 balloons equally between 3 clowns.
How many balloons each?

Which is right?

Circle the sums with answers that match
the numbers at the top of each box.

3
6 ÷ 3
22 ÷ 2
25 ÷ 5
27 ÷ 9

10
12 ÷ 4
32 ÷ 8
60 ÷ 6
10 ÷ 5

8
64 ÷ 8
72 ÷ 12
18 ÷ 6
81 ÷ 9

4
36 ÷ 9
20 ÷ 2
16 ÷ 8
12 ÷ 4

6
50 ÷ 10
96 ÷ 12
18 ÷ 9
24 ÷ 4

7
88 ÷ 11
28 ÷ 4
12 ÷ 6
72 ÷ 9

Groups

Draw rings around the following things to divide them into groups.

GROUPS OF 2

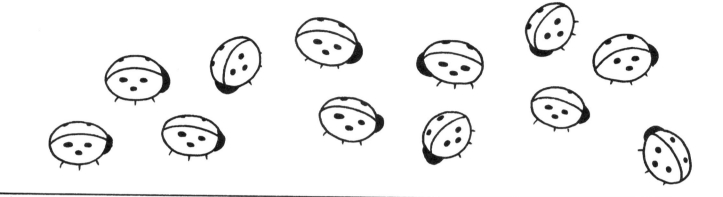

GROUPS OF 4

GROUPS OF 3

Division test

Do the sums and write the answers in the boxes.
Check your answers by looking at the tables.

$6 \div 3 =$ ☐

$14 \div 2 =$ ☐

$25 \div 5 =$ ☐

$27 \div 9 =$ ☐

$4 \div 2 =$ ☐

$64 \div 8 =$ ☐

$40 \div 4 =$ ☐

$5 \div 5 =$ ☐

$21 \div 7 =$ ☐

$8 \div 2 =$ ☐

$9 \div 1 =$ ☐

$44 \div 11 =$ ☐

$20 \div 2 =$

$45 \div 5 =$

$24 \div 4 =$

$35 \div 7 =$

$18 \div 6 =$

$3 \div 3 =$

$36 \div 6 =$

$15 \div 5 =$

$70 \div 7 =$

$16 \div 8 =$

$28 \div 4 =$

$12 \div 3 =$

$56 \div 7 =$

$50 \div 10 =$

Answers

Multiplication sums

$3 \times 8 = 24$ $5 \times 6 = 30$ $7 \times 2 = 14$

Missing numbers

$2 \times 2 = 4$	$4 \times 4 = 16$
$3 \times 5 = 15$	$7 \times 8 = 56$
$7 \times 2 = 14$	$2 \times 4 = 8$
$3 \times 3 = 9$	$11 \times 3 = 33$
$6 \times 5 = 30$	$9 \times 5 = 45$
$9 \times 2 = 18$	$6 \times 6 = 36$
$4 \times 5 = 20$	$8 \times 3 = 24$
$1 \times 3 = 3$	$4 \times 7 = 28$

$12 \times 5 = 60$	$11 \times 10 = 110$
$10 \times 3 = 30$	$6 \times 8 = 48$
$4 \times 3 = 12$	$6 \times 4 = 24$
$1 \times 11 = 11$	$7 \times 9 = 63$
$8 \times 5 = 40$	$2 \times 2 = 4$
$9 \times 3 = 27$	$12 \times 8 = 96$
$8 \times 9 = 72$	$9 \times 9 = 81$
$12 \times 12 = 144$	$3 \times 7 = 21$

Missing bees

$3 \times 4 = 12$ $2 \times 3 = 6$ $8 \times 2 = 16$

Sum ladders

$3 \times 2 = 6$ $5 \times 5 = 25$ $9 \times 6 = 54$

Flower sums

$3 \times 0 = 0$ $3 \times 4 = 12$ $5 \times 2 = 10$

Magical numbers

$3 \times 3 = 9$ $4 \times 6 = 24$ $10 \times 9 = 90$

Sums puzzles

Sums crossword

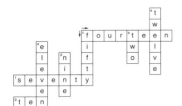

Match the answers

$7 \times 8 = 56$	$9 \times 9 = 81$	$3 \times 3 = 9$
$5 \times 6 = 30$	$4 \times 12 = 48$	$7 \times 3 = 21$

Butterfly sums

$6 \div 2 = 3$ $4 \div 2 = 2$ $10 \div 2 = 5$

Missing numbers

$4 \div 4 = 1$	$12 \div 6 = 2$
$8 \div 4 = 2$	$36 \div 9 = 4$
$21 \div 7 = 3$	$9 \div 9 = 1$
$54 \div 6 = 9$	$56 \div 7 = 8$
$36 \div 6 = 6$	$42 \div 7 = 6$
$63 \div 9 = 7$	$18 \div 6 = 3$
$49 \div 7 = 7$	$20 \div 4 = 5$
$99 \div 9 = 11$	$28 \div 7 = 4$

$24 \div 6 = 4$	$30 \div 6 = 5$
$18 \div 9 = 2$	$10 \div 5 = 2$
$70 \div 7 = 10$	$72 \div 8 = 9$
$99 \div 9 = 11$	$40 \div 5 = 8$
$48 \div 6 = 8$	$90 \div 10 = 9$
$27 \div 9 = 3$	$56 \div 8 = 7$
$32 \div 4 = 8$	$6 \div 3 = 2$
$45 \div 9 = 5$	$24 \div 8 = 3$

Star sums

$81 \div 9 = 9$	$35 \div 5 = 7$	$49 \div 7 = 7$
$12 \div 6 = 2$	$20 \div 5 = 4$	$3 \div 3 = 1$
$32 \div 4 = 8$	$55 \div 11 = 5$	

Juggling sums

$6 \div 3 = 2$	$42 \div 7 = 6$	$27 \div 3 = 9$
$9 \div 1 = 9$	$16 \div 2 = 8$	$24 \div 4 = 6$
$30 \div 5 = 6$	$63 \div 9 = 7$	

Solve these problems

Each child would have 4 books.
Each child would have 2 ice creams.
There would be 1 left over.
Each rabbit would have 4 carrots.
Each monkey would have 2 bananas.
Each elephant would have 4 buns.
There would be 1 left over.
Each clown would have 3 balloons.

Which is right?

$27 \div 9 = 3$	$60 \div 6 = 10$	$64 \div 8 = 8$
$36 \div 9 = 4$	$24 \div 4 = 6$	$28 \div 4 = 7$

Times Tables

1 × 9 =
2 × 9 =
3 × 9 =
4 × 9 =
5 × 9 =
6 × 9 =
7 × 9 =
8 × 9 =
9 × 9 =
10 × 9 =
11 × 9 =
12 × 9 =

1 and 2 times tables

Complete these multiplication tables.

1 x 1 =		1 x 2 =	
2 x 1 =		2 x 2 =	
3 x 1 =		3 x 2 =	
4 x 1 =		4 x 2 =	
5 x 1 =		5 x 2 =	
6 x 1 =		6 x 2 =	
7 x 1 =		7 x 2 =	
8 x 1 =		8 x 2 =	
9 x 1 =		9 x 2 =	
10 x 1 =		10 x 2 =	
11 x 1 =		11 x 2 =	
12 x 1 =		12 x 2 =	

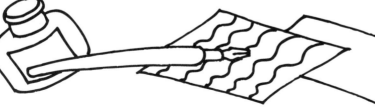
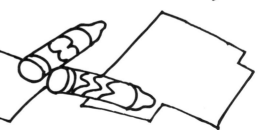

3 and 4 times tables

Complete these multiplication tables.

1 x 3 =		1 x 4 =
2 x 3 =		2 x 4 =
3 x 3 =		3 x 4 =
4 x 3 =		4 x 4 =
5 x 3 =		5 x 4 =
6 x 3 =		6 x 4 =
7 x 3 =		7 x 4 =
8 x 3 =		8 x 4 =
9 x 3 =		9 x 4 =
10 x 3 =		10 x 4 =
11 x 3 =		11 x 4 =
12 x 3 =		12 x 4 =

5 and 6 times tables

Complete these multiplication tables.

1 x 5 =	1 x 6 =
2 x 5 =	2 x 6 =
3 x 5 =	3 x 6 =
4 x 5 =	4 x 6 =
5 x 5 =	5 x 6 =
6 x 5 =	6 x 6 =
7 x 5 =	7 x 6 =
8 x 5 =	8 x 6 =
9 x 5 =	9 x 6 =
10 x 5 =	10 x 6 =
11 x 5 =	11 x 6 =
12 x 5 =	12 x 6 =

7 and 8 times tables

Complete these multiplication tables.

1 x 7 = ☐		1 x 8 = ☐
2 x 7 = ☐		2 x 8 = ☐
3 x 7 = ☐		3 x 8 = ☐
4 x 7 = ☐		4 x 8 = ☐
5 x 7 = ☐		5 x 8 = ☐
6 x 7 = ☐		6 x 8 = ☐
7 x 7 = ☐		7 x 8 = ☐
8 x 7 = ☐		8 x 8 = ☐
9 x 7 = ☐		9 x 8 = ☐
10 x 7 = ☐		10 x 8 = ☐
11 x 7 = ☐		11 x 8 = ☐
12 x 7 = ☐		12 x 8 = ☐

9 and 10 times tables
Complete these multiplication tables.

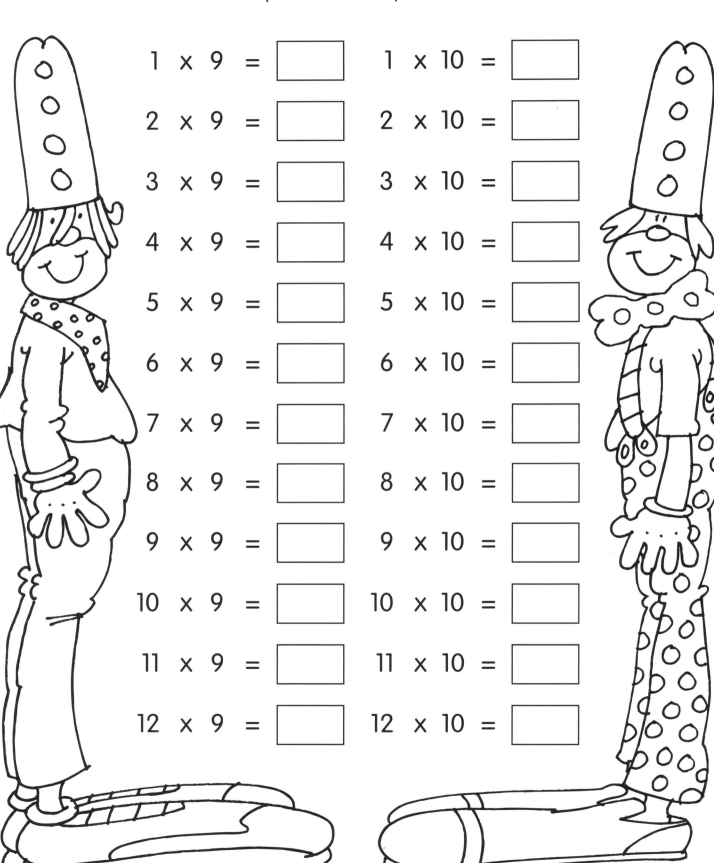

1 x 9 = ☐   1 x 10 = ☐

2 x 9 = ☐   2 x 10 = ☐

3 x 9 = ☐   3 x 10 = ☐

4 x 9 = ☐   4 x 10 = ☐

5 x 9 = ☐   5 x 10 = ☐

6 x 9 = ☐   6 x 10 = ☐

7 x 9 = ☐   7 x 10 = ☐

8 x 9 = ☐   8 x 10 = ☐

9 x 9 = ☐   9 x 10 = ☐

10 x 9 = ☐   10 x 10 = ☐

11 x 9 = ☐   11 x 10 = ☐

12 x 9 = ☐   12 x 10 = ☐

11 and 12 times tables

Complete these multiplication tables.

1 x 11 =		1 x 12 =	
2 x 11 =		2 x 12 =	
3 x 11 =		3 x 12 =	
4 x 11 =		4 x 12 =	
5 x 11 =		5 x 12 =	
6 x 11 =		6 x 12 =	
7 x 11 =		7 x 12 =	
8 x 11 =		8 x 12 =	
9 x 11 =		9 x 12 =	
10 x 11 =		10 x 12 =	
11 x 11 =		11 x 12 =	
12 x 11 =		12 x 12 =	

Picture sums

Work out the sums and write the answers.

Creepy crawly sums

Write the numbers to complete the sums.

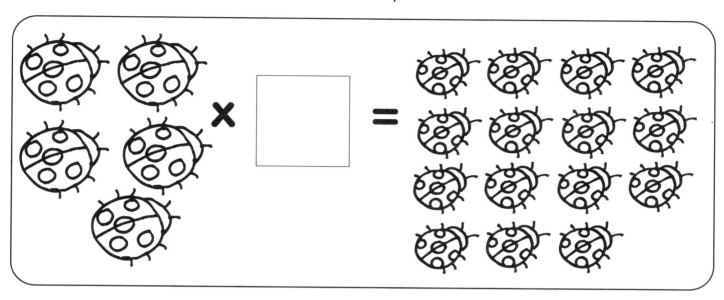

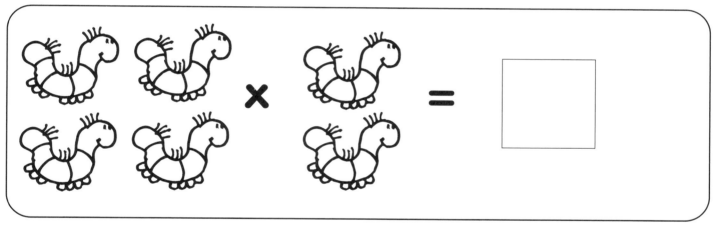

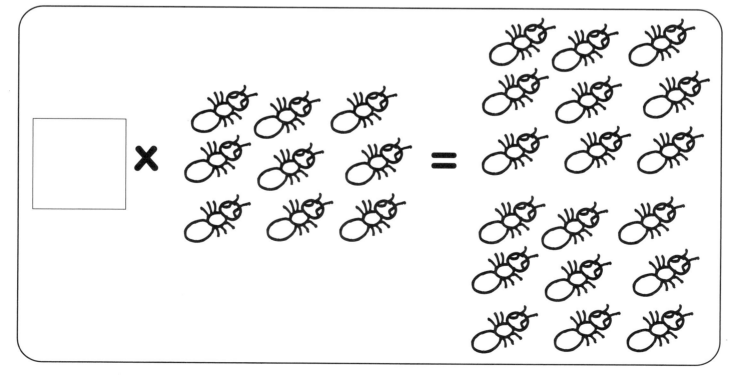

Metal multiplication

Complete these robot sums.

6 × 6 =

× 5 = 45

10 × = 60

Sums puzzles

Do the sums to complete these puzzles.

	×	3	=	9
×	■	×	■	×
1	×	2	=	
=	■	=	■	=
3	×		=	18

5	×		=	10
×	■	×	■	×
	×		=	5
=	■	=	■	=
5	×	10	=	

Snakes and ladders

Do the sums in the snakes and ladders.

10 × 4 =

11 × 8 =

3 × 4 =

8 × 7 =

Galaxy gazing

Do the sums to join the aliens with their planets.

Shooting stars

Do the sums to join the fairies with their shooting stars.

Sums puzzles

Do the sums to complete these puzzles.

Sums wordsearch

Do the sums and find the missing numbers in the wordsearch grid.
You can read across and down.
Circle the words as you find them.

$9 \times \boxed{} = 81$ $\boxed{} \times 4 = 36$

$\boxed{} \times 7 = 56$ $\boxed{} \times 1 = 11$

$6 \times 10 = \boxed{}$ $7 \times 2 = \boxed{}$

$4 \times 5 = \boxed{}$ $1 \times 13 = \boxed{}$

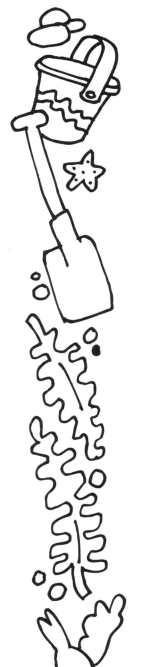

T	H	I	R	T	E	E	N	F
W	U	I	L	O	P	I	W	O
E	L	E	V	E	N	U	O	U
N	O	P	E	S	I	L	E	R
T	H	A	H	E	N	J	A	T
Y	I	N	I	N	E	D	T	E
N	R	F	S	H	B	I	P	E
S	I	X	T	Y	E	N	N	N
L	G	A	E	E	W	S	A	R
A	W	E	I	G	H	T	C	A

Painting problems

Do the sums in the ladders and write the answers on the buckets.

Sums crossword

Do the sums and write the answers in the crossword grid.

$1 \rightarrow \quad 8 \times 2 = \square$ $4 \quad 2 \times 4 = \square$

$1 \downarrow \quad 17 \times 1 = \square$ $5 \quad 11 \times 1 = \square$

$2 \quad 3 \times 3 = \square$ $6 \quad 1 \times 1 = \square$

$3 \rightarrow \quad 1 \times 2 = \square$ $7 \quad 10 \times 8 = \square$

$3 \downarrow \quad 4 \times 3 = \square$ $8 \quad 9 \times 10 = \square$

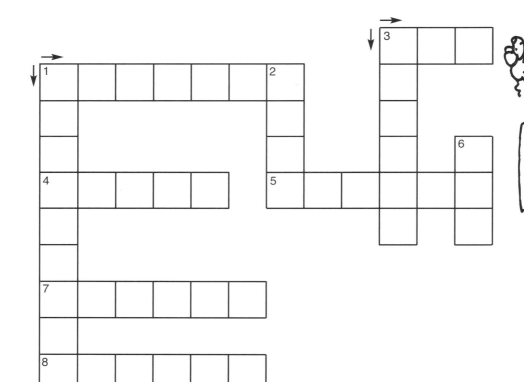

Puzzling problems

Help Wanda Witch solve these puzzling problems.

If 1 bag of slime makes 3 cups of love potion, how many cups of potion can Wanda make with 3 bags of slime?

If Wanda makes 4 test tubes of hate potion in 1 hour, how many tubes will she make in 2 hours?

If 5 wizards each buy 5 of Wanda's jealousy pills, how many jealousy pills will she sell altogether?

Sums wordsearch

Do the sums and find the answers in the wordsearch grid.
You can read across and down.
Circle the words as you find them.

12 x 1 = ☐	8 x 1 = ☐
5 x 4 = ☐	3 x 3 = ☐
7 x 2 = ☐	11 x 1 = ☐
1 x 1 = ☐	4 x 4 = ☐

T	W	E	L	V	E	R	S	F
W	A	M	L	B	P	I	W	O
E	K	W	H	O	N	E	H	U
N	I	N	E	S	T	L	E	R
T	H	A	I	E	U	E	A	T
Y	I	T	G	S	C	V	T	E
E	R	F	H	H	B	E	P	E
S	I	X	T	E	E	N	N	N
L	G	A	T	E	W	S	A	R
A	D	U	G	W	G	E	C	A

Computer crazy

Put a tick next to the sums that are right and a cross next
to those that are wrong.

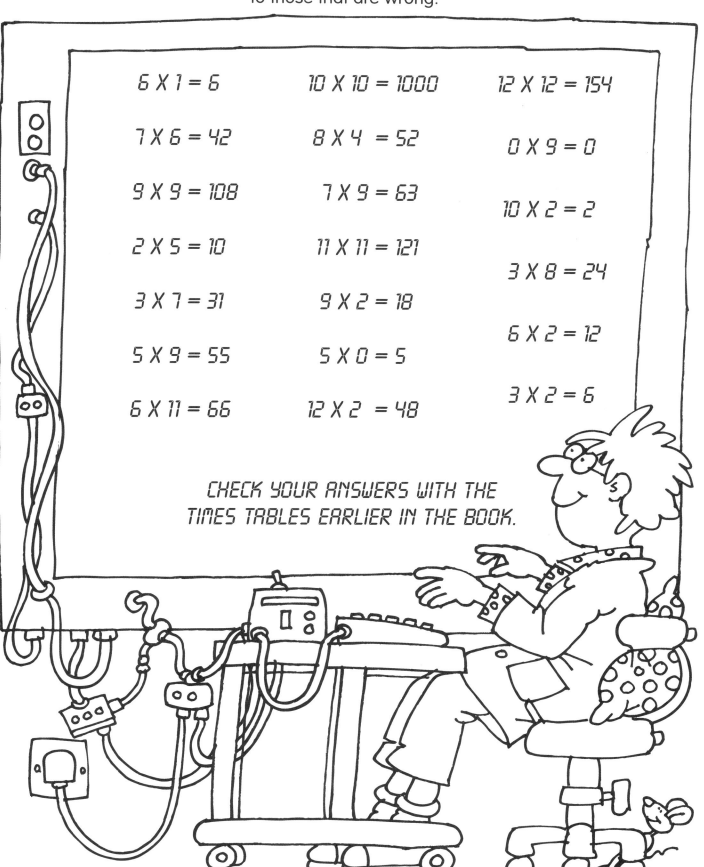

6 X 1 = 6	10 X 10 = 1000	12 X 12 = 154
7 X 6 = 42	8 X 4 = 52	0 X 9 = 0
9 X 9 = 108	7 X 9 = 63	10 X 2 = 2
2 X 5 = 10	11 X 11 = 121	3 X 8 = 24
3 X 7 = 31	9 X 2 = 18	6 X 2 = 12
5 X 9 = 55	5 X 0 = 5	3 X 2 = 6
6 X 11 = 66	12 X 2 = 48	

CHECK YOUR ANSWERS WITH THE
TIMES TABLES EARLIER IN THE BOOK.

Sums crossword

Do the sums and write the answers in the crossword grid.

1   10 x 7 = ☐   6   1 x 2 = ☐

2   9 x 2 = ☐   7   4 x 3 = ☐

3   1 x 13 = ☐   8   11 x 1 = ☐

4   5 x 0 = ☐   9   4 x 2 = ☐

5   1 x 1 = ☐   10   10 x 9 = ☐

Right or wrong?

Put a tick next to the sums that are right and a cross next
to those that are wrong.

6 X 4 = 24   7 X 3 = 21   12 X 10 = 120

5 X 5 = 35   12 X 4 = 28   5 X 8 = 45

7 X 2 = 14   10 X 3 = 3   3 X 3 = 9

8 X 9 = 64   9 X 6 = 34   5 X 10 = 50

6 X 2 = 12   9 X 9 = 81   8 X 3 = 34

4 X 3 = 12   7 X 7 = 49   5 X 11 = 55

CHECK YOUR ANSWERS WITH THE
TIMES TABLES EARLIER IN THE BOOK.

Sums puzzles

Do the sums to complete these puzzles.

3	×		=	6
×		×		×
	×	2	=	8
=		=		=
12	×		=	

	×	5	=	5
×		×		×
4	×		=	8
=		=		=
4	×	10	=	

Sums crossword

Do the sums and write the answers in the crossword grid.

1   $6 \times 3 =$ ☐   5→ $1 \times 5 =$ ☐

2   $6 \times 2 =$ ☐   5↓ $7 \times 2 =$ ☐

3→ $10 \times 10 =$ ☐   6 $7 \times 10 =$ ☐

3↓ $1 \times 1 =$ ☐   7→ $5 \times 2 =$ ☐

4   $4 \times 2 =$ ☐   7↓ $5 \times 4 =$ ☐

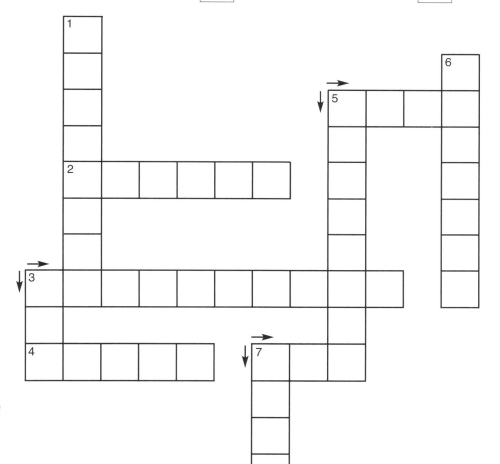

Problem solving

Help Arthur the Astronaut solve these solar system problems.

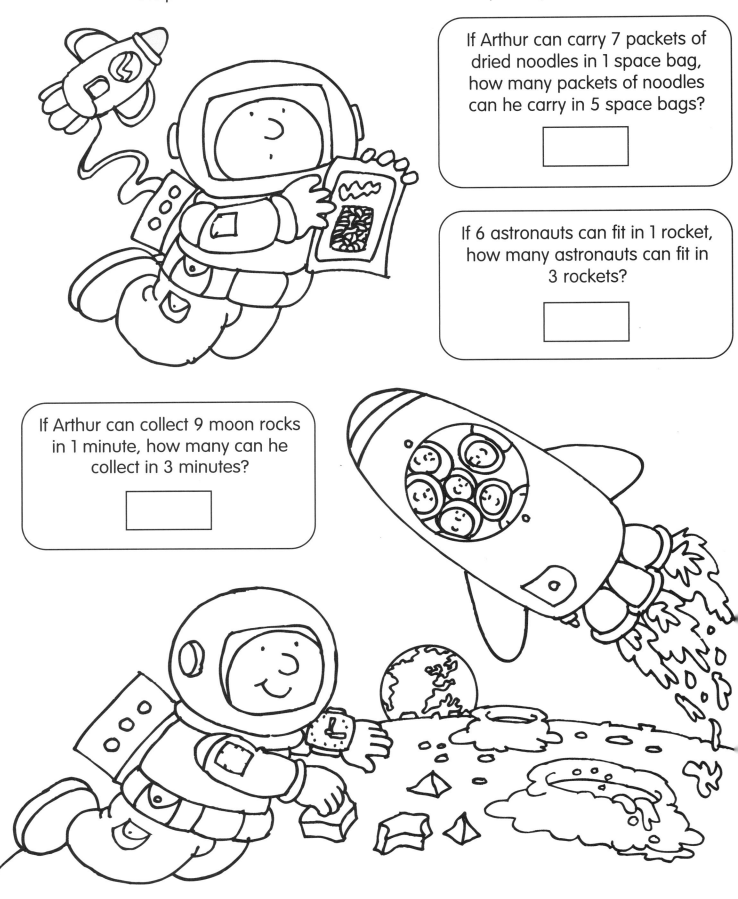

If Arthur can carry 7 packets of dried noodles in 1 space bag, how many packets of noodles can he carry in 5 space bags?

If 6 astronauts can fit in 1 rocket, how many astronauts can fit in 3 rockets?

If Arthur can collect 9 moon rocks in 1 minute, how many can he collect in 3 minutes?

Jungle Jim

Jungle Jim wants to get back to his tree house. Help him swing through the jungle by colouring the three vines whose numbers are in the 6, 8 and 9 times tables.

Sums wordsearch

Do the sums and find the missing numbers in the wordsearch grid.
You can read across and down.
Circle the words as you find them.

8 x 2 = ☐   12 x ☐ = 144

☐ x 4 = 12   3 x 5 = ☐

6 x ☐ = 36   ☐ x 1 = 18

3 x ☐ = 27   10 x 5 = ☐

S	I	X	T	E	E	N	S	F
I	A	M	H	B	P	N	W	I
X	K	W	R	O	N	I	H	F
N	O	N	E	S	T	N	E	T
T	T	W	E	L	V	E	A	E
Y	I	T	E	S	C	N	T	E
E	R	F	H	H	B	T	P	N
S	V	F	I	F	T	Y	N	I
L	G	A	T	E	W	S	A	R
E	I	G	H	T	E	E	N	A

Test time 1

Do these sums.

$2 \times 3 = \boxed{}$ $5 \times 8 = \boxed{}$

$5 \times 7 = \boxed{}$ $2 \times 5 = \boxed{}$

$6 \times 6 = \boxed{}$ $10 \times 5 = \boxed{}$

$12 \times 4 = \boxed{}$ $6 \times 8 = \boxed{}$

$7 \times 0 = \boxed{}$ $11 \times 10 = \boxed{}$

$8 \times 10 = \boxed{}$ $6 \times 9 = \boxed{}$

$9 \times 8 = \boxed{}$ $1 \times 1 = \boxed{}$

$2 \times 2 = \boxed{}$ $12 \times 0 = \boxed{}$

$1 \times 7 = \boxed{}$ $5 \times 2 = \boxed{}$

$11 \times 6 = \boxed{}$ $2 \times 8 = \boxed{}$

$5 \times 9 = \boxed{}$ $9 \times 4 = \boxed{}$

$9 \times 2 = \boxed{}$ $6 \times 3 = \boxed{}$

Test time 2

Complete these sums.

$3 \times 0 = \boxed{}$

$4 \times 4 = \boxed{}$

$9 \times \boxed{} = 18$

$\boxed{} \times 8 = 40$

$\boxed{} \times 7 = 49$

$6 \times \boxed{} = 12$

$4 \times \boxed{} = 32$

$\boxed{} \times 9 = 81$

$12 \times 6 = \boxed{}$

$5 \times \boxed{} = 40$

$\boxed{} \times 7 = 77$

$8 \times \boxed{} = 64$

$\boxed{} \times 3 = 21$

$5 \times 9 = \boxed{}$

$11 \times \boxed{} = 0$

$9 \times 8 = \boxed{}$

$\boxed{} \times 6 = 24$

$6 \times 1 = \boxed{}$

$\boxed{} \times 3 = 30$

$2 \times \boxed{} = 14$

$7 \times \boxed{} = 56$

$\boxed{} \times 12 = 144$

$2 \times \boxed{} = 10$

$9 \times \boxed{} = 27$

Answers

1 and 2 times tables

1	x	1	=	1
2	x	1	=	2
3	x	1	=	3
4	x	1	=	4
5	x	1	=	5
6	x	1	=	6
7	x	1	=	7
8	x	1	=	8
9	x	1	=	9
10	x	1	=	10
11	x	1	=	11
12	x	1	=	12

1	x	2	=	2
2	x	2	=	4
3	x	2	=	6
4	x	2	=	8
5	x	2	=	10
6	x	2	=	12
7	x	2	=	14
8	x	2	=	16
9	x	2	=	18
10	x	2	=	20
11	x	2	=	22
12	x	2	=	24

3 and 4 times tables

1	x	3	=	3
2	x	3	=	6
3	x	3	=	9
4	x	3	=	12
5	x	3	=	15
6	x	3	=	18
7	x	3	=	21
8	x	3	=	24
9	x	3	=	27
10	x	3	=	30
11	x	3	=	33
12	x	3	=	36

1	x	4	=	4
2	x	4	=	8
3	x	4	=	12
4	x	4	=	16
5	x	4	=	20
6	x	4	=	24
7	x	4	=	28
8	x	4	=	32
9	x	4	=	36
10	x	4	=	40
11	x	4	=	44
12	x	4	=	48

5 and 6 times tables

1	x	5	=	5
2	x	5	=	10
3	x	5	=	15
4	x	5	=	20
5	x	5	=	25
6	x	5	=	30
7	x	5	=	35
8	x	5	=	40
9	x	5	=	45
10	x	5	=	50
11	x	5	=	55
12	x	5	=	60

1	x	6	=	6
2	x	6	=	12
3	x	6	=	18
4	x	6	=	24
5	x	6	=	30
6	x	6	=	36
7	x	6	=	42
8	x	6	=	48
9	x	6	=	54
10	x	6	=	60
11	x	6	=	66
12	x	6	=	72

7 and 8 times tables

1	x	7	=	7
2	x	7	=	14
3	x	7	=	21
4	x	7	=	28
5	x	7	=	35
6	x	7	=	42
7	x	7	=	49
8	x	7	=	56
9	x	7	=	63
10	x	7	=	70
11	x	7	=	77
12	x	7	=	84

1	x	8	=	8
2	x	8	=	16
3	x	8	=	24
4	x	8	=	32
5	x	8	=	40
6	x	8	=	48
7	x	8	=	56
8	x	8	=	64
9	x	8	=	72
10	x	8	=	80
11	x	8	=	88
12	x	8	=	96

9 and 10 times tables

1	x	9	=	9
2	x	9	=	18
3	x	9	=	27
4	x	9	=	36
5	x	9	=	45
6	x	9	=	54
7	x	9	=	63
8	x	9	=	72
9	x	9	=	81
10	x	9	=	90
11	x	9	=	99
12	x	9	=	108

1	x	10	=	10
2	x	10	=	20
3	x	10	=	30
4	x	10	=	40
5	x	10	=	50
6	x	10	=	60
7	x	10	=	70
8	x	10	=	80
9	x	10	=	90
10	x	10	=	100
11	x	10	=	110
12	x	10	=	120

11 and 12 times tables

1	x	11	=	11
2	x	11	=	22
3	x	11	=	33
4	x	11	=	44
5	x	11	=	55
6	x	11	=	66
7	x	11	=	77
8	x	11	=	88
9	x	11	=	99
10	x	11	=	110
11	x	11	=	121
12	x	11	=	132

1	x	12	=	12
2	x	12	=	24
3	x	12	=	36
4	x	12	=	48
5	x	12	=	60
6	x	12	=	72
7	x	12	=	84
8	x	12	=	96
9	x	12	=	108
10	x	12	=	120
11	x	12	=	132
12	x	12	=	144

Picture sums

4 x 3 = 12   7 x 5 = 35   6 x 6 = 36

Creepy crawly sums

5 x 3 = 15   4 x 2 = 8   2 x 9 = 18

Metal multiplication

6 x 6 = 36   9 x 5 = 45   10 x 6 = 60

Sums puzzles

3	x	3	=	9
x		x		x
1	x	2	=	2
=		=		=
3	x	6	=	18

5	x	2	=	10
x		x		x
1	x	5	=	5
=		=		=
5	x	10	=	50

Snakes and ladders

10 x 4 = 40   11 x 8 = 88   3 x 4 = 12
8 x 7 = 56

Galaxy gazing

7 x 2 = 14   9 x 3 = 27   2 x 1 = 2
6 x 6 = 36   5 x 8 = 40   7 x 5 = 35
12 x 4 = 48   5 x 3 = 15

Shooting stars

3 × 7 = 21   2 × 2 = 4   8 × 0 = 0
6 × 8 = 48   10 × 2 = 20   3 × 3 = 9
4 × 4 = 16   5 × 9 = 45

Sums puzzles

3	x	4	=	12
x		x		x
3	x	2	=	6
=		=		=
9	x	8	=	72

6	x	2	=	12
x		x		x
1	x	3	=	3
=		=		=
6	x	6	=	36

Sums wordsearch

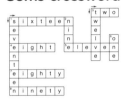

Painting problems

9 × 9 = 81   6 × 12 = 72   5 × 6 = 30

Sums crossword

Puzzling problems

9 cups of potion   8 test tubes   25 pills

Sums wordsearch

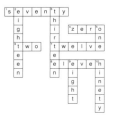

Computer crazy

6 × 1 = 6 ✔   10 × 10 = 1000 ✘   12 × 12 = 154 ✘
7 × 6 = 42 ✔   8 × 4 = 52 ✘   0 × 9 = 0 ✔
9 × 9 = 108 ✘   7 × 9 = 63 ✔   10 × 2 = 2 ✘
2 × 5 = 10 ✔   11 × 11 = 121 ✔   3 × 8 = 24 ✔
3 × 7 = 31 ✘   9 × 2 = 18 ✔   6 × 2 = 12 ✔
5 × 9 = 55 ✘   5 × 0 = 5 ✘   3 × 2 = 6 ✔
6 × 11 = 66 ✔   12 × 2 = 48 ✘

Sums crossword

Right or wrong?

6 × 4 = 24 ✔   7 × 3 = 21 ✔   12 × 10 = 120 ✔
5 × 5 = 35 ✘   12 × 4 = 28 ✘   5 × 8 = 45 ✘
7 × 2 = 14 ✔   10 × 3 = 3 ✘   3 × 3 = 9 ✔
8 × 9 = 64 ✘   9 × 6 = 34 ✘   5 × 10 = 50 ✔
6 × 2 = 12 ✔   9 × 9 = 81 ✔   8 × 3 = 34 ✘
4 × 3 = 12 ✔   7 × 7 = 49 ✔   5 × 11 = 55 ✔

Sums puzzles

3	x	2	=	6
x		x		x
4	x	2	=	8
=		=		=
12	x	4	=	48

1	x	5	=	5
x		x		x
4	x	2	=	8
=		=		=
4	x	10	=	40

Sums crossword

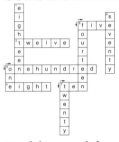

Problem solving

35 packets   18 astronauts   27 rocks

Jungle Jim

6 12 18 24 30 36 42   16 24 32 40 48 56 64
27 36 45 54 63 72 81

Sums wordsearch

Test time 1

2 × 3 = 6   5 × 8 = 40   5 × 7 = 35
2 × 5 = 10   6 × 6 = 36   10 × 5 = 50
12 × 4 = 48   6 × 8 = 48   7 × 0 = 0
11 × 10 = 110   8 × 10 = 80   6 × 9 = 54
9 × 8 = 72   1 × 1 = 1   2 × 2 = 4
12 × 0 = 0   1 × 7 = 7   5 × 2 = 10
11 × 6 = 66   2 × 8 = 16   5 × 9 = 45
9 × 4 = 36   9 × 2 = 18   6 × 3 = 18

Test time 2

3 × 0 = 0   7 × 3 = 21   4 × 4 = 16
5 × 9 = 45   9 × 2 = 18   11 × 0 = 0
5 × 8 = 40   9 × 8 = 72   7 × 7 = 49
4 × 6 = 24   6 × 2 = 12   6 × 1 = 6
4 × 8 = 32   10 × 3 = 30   9 × 9 = 81
2 × 7 = 14   12 × 6 = 72   7 × 8 = 56
5 × 8 = 40   12 × 12 = 144   11 × 7 = 77
2 × 5 = 10   8 × 8 = 64   9 × 3 = 27

Mental Maths

Pet problems

Do these sums.

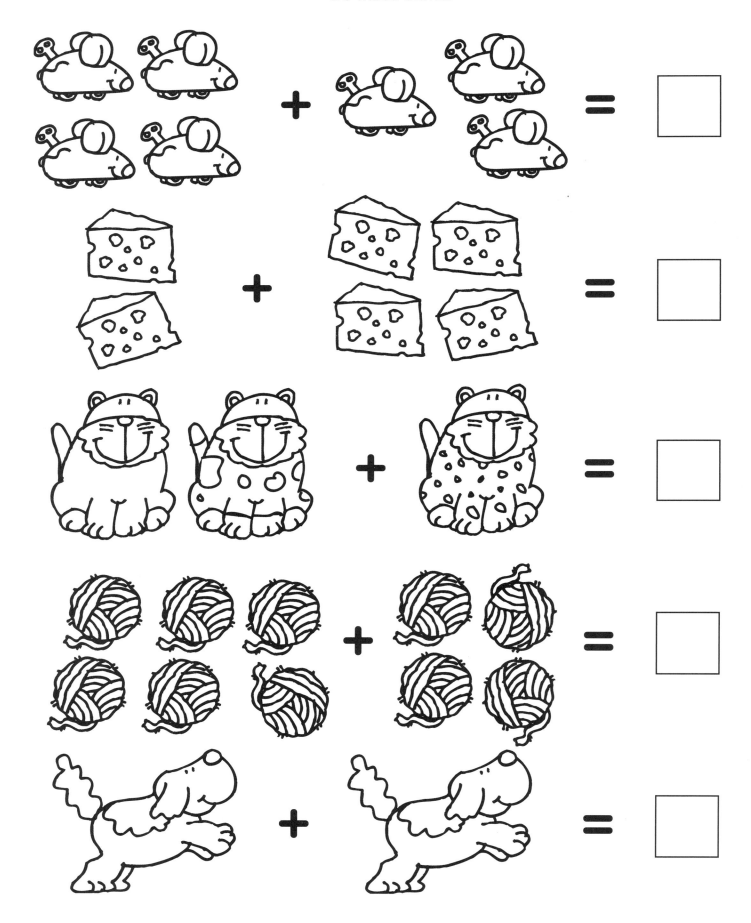

Adding numbers

As quickly as you can, add these numbers in your head and say the answers aloud.

7 add 2

11 add 11

4 plus 4

9 plus 7

6 and 6

12 + 12

3 add 8

6 and 5

9 plus 4

eight plus two

7 + 7

9 add 8

5 and 5

11 plus 12

10 + 11

4 and 8

8 + 7

one add six

6 plus 8

5 + 10

Farmyard frolics

Answer these adding stories.

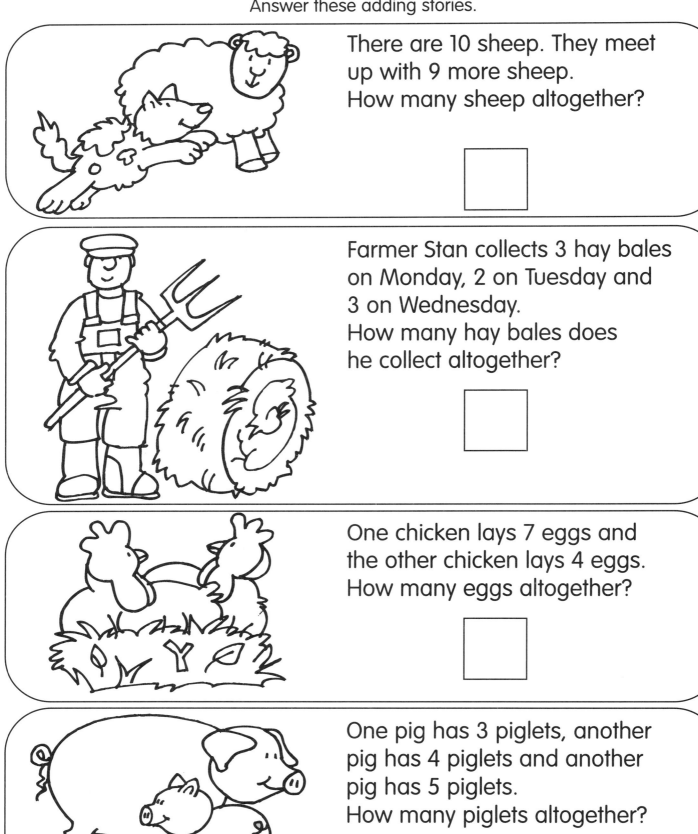

There are 10 sheep. They meet up with 9 more sheep.
How many sheep altogether?

Farmer Stan collects 3 hay bales on Monday, 2 on Tuesday and 3 on Wednesday.
How many hay bales does he collect altogether?

One chicken lays 7 eggs and the other chicken lays 4 eggs.
How many eggs altogether?

One pig has 3 piglets, another pig has 4 piglets and another pig has 5 piglets.
How many piglets altogether?

Pyramid puzzlers

Complete these adding pyramids. The first one has been done for you.

13

8 5

6 2 3

4 3 1

7 3 2

9 2 1

6 5 6

3 3 3

Brain teasers

As quickly as you can, try answering these problems in your head.

1 more than 5 is

2 more than 3 is

4 more than 6 is

5 more than 5 is

9 more than 3 is

7 more than 7 is

11 more than 9 is

8 more than 4 is

3 more than 2 is

10 more than 12 is

4 more than 2 is

9 more than 6 is

Making 20

Draw horizontal or vertical lines to join two numbers next to each other that total 20.
You can use any of the numbers more than once.

7	2	19	1	4	7	14	3	17	3
11	19	20	4	16	15	7	2	15	1
9	15	5	1	2	8	5	15	3	0
5	3	12	2	2	6	20	19	17	19
10	13	2	18	0	12	20	0	6	20
10	20	5	9	4	5	0	1	14	6
10	15	2	16	16	4	3	6	6	7
11	4	13	7	1	6	1	19	7	1
3	9	8	2	4	0	19	7	8	8
6	11	9	0	2	20	2	3	0	1
1	1	7	5	3	0	2	6	11	9

Fishing for 20

As quickly as you can,
draw lines to join the numbers on the penguins
and fish that together total 20.
The first one has been done for you.

Seaside subtraction

Work out the sums and write the answers in the boxes.

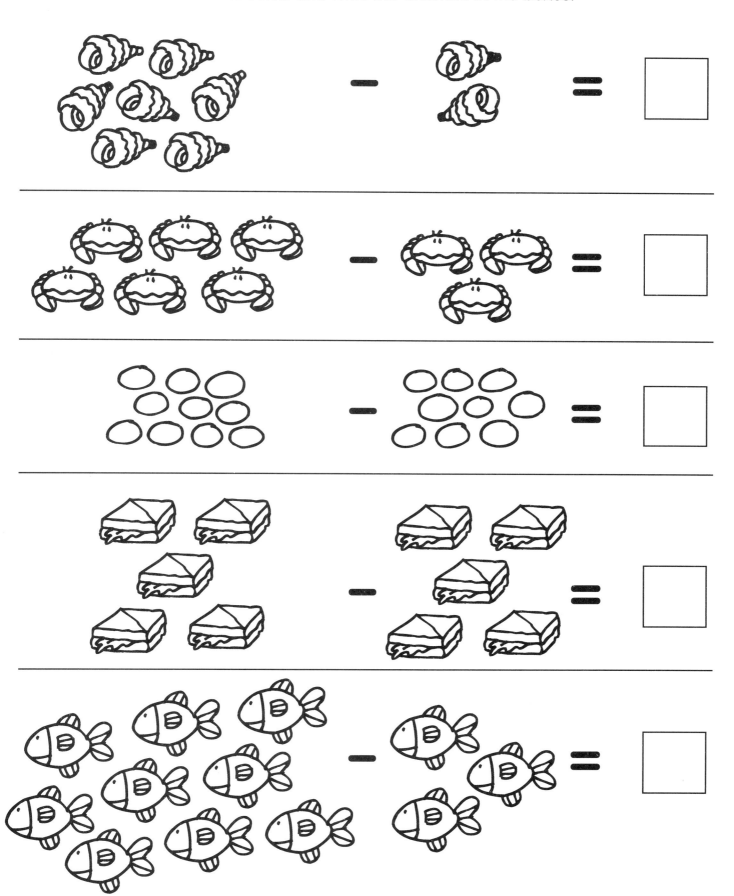

Subtracting numbers

Subtract these numbers in your head and write the answers.

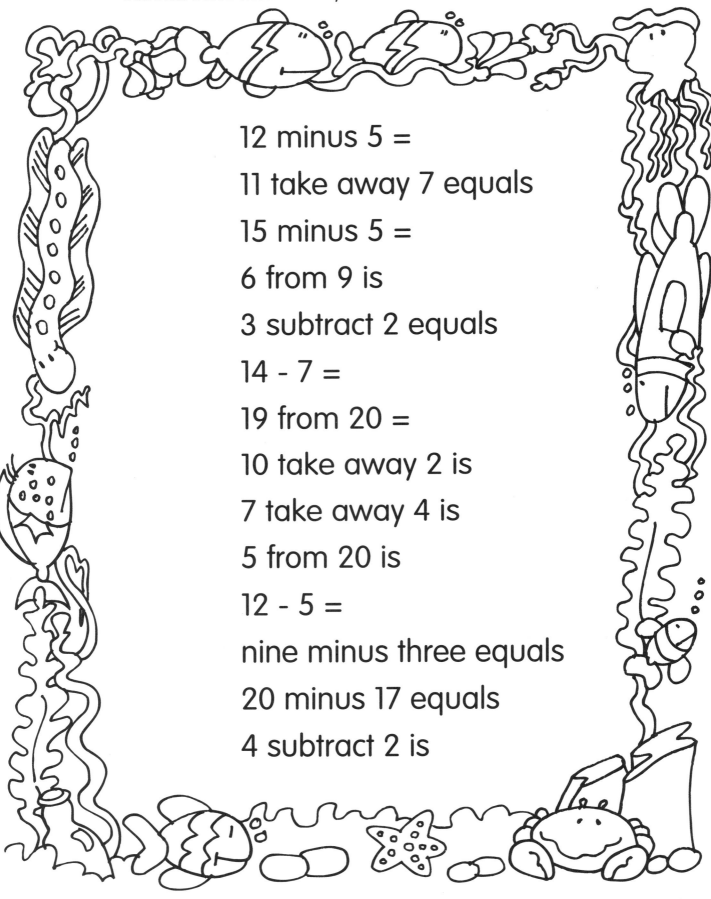

12 minus 5 =

11 take away 7 equals

15 minus 5 =

6 from 9 is

3 subtract 2 equals

14 - 7 =

19 from 20 =

10 take away 2 is

7 take away 4 is

5 from 20 is

12 - 5 =

nine minus three equals

20 minus 17 equals

4 subtract 2 is

Pond problems

Answer these subtracting stories.

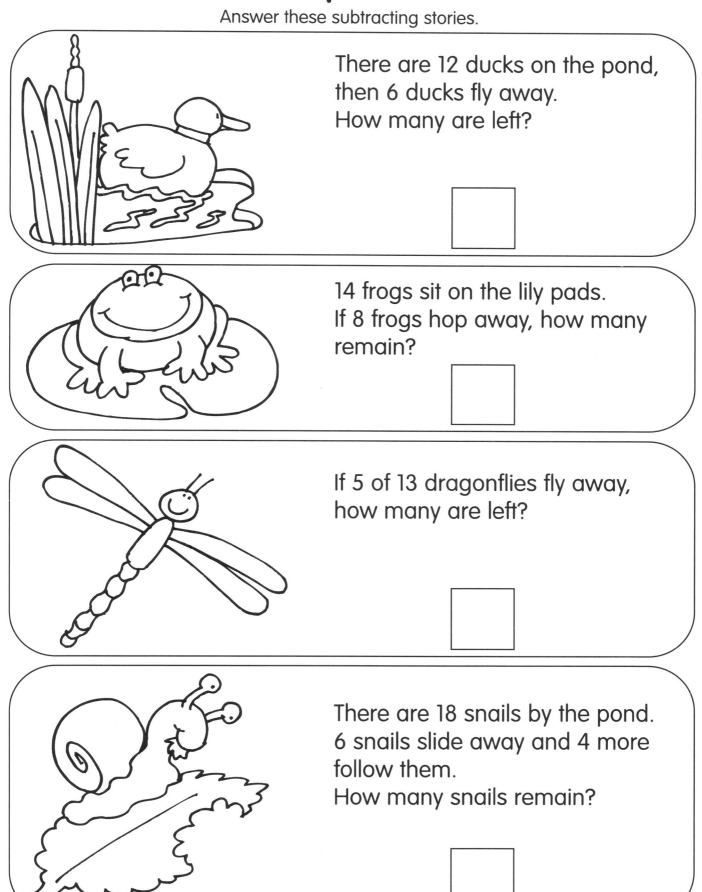

There are 12 ducks on the pond,
then 6 ducks fly away.
How many are left?

14 frogs sit on the lily pads.
If 8 frogs hop away, how many
remain?

If 5 of 13 dragonflies fly away,
how many are left?

There are 18 snails by the pond.
6 snails slide away and 4 more
follow them.
How many snails remain?

Baby blocks

Complete these subtracting blocks. The first one has been done for you.

Computer crazy

Colin the computer is feeling tired. Help him finish this table of calculations.
The first one has been done for you.

START	ADD	EQUALS	SUBTRACT	TOTAL
3	2	5	1	4
2	1	_	2	_
6	_	8	4	_
5	5	_	5	_
1	_	11	_	6
4	6	_	6	_

Number patterns

Complete these number patterns.

1 __ 3 __ 5 __ 7

__ 9 __ 7 __ 5 __

2 __ 6 __ 10 __ 14

__ 6 __ 12 __ 18 __

4 __ 12 __ 20 __ 28

__ 10 __ 20 __ 30 __

100 __ 98 __ 96 __ 94

49 __ 35 __ 21 __ 7

Number trails

Do the sums and write the answers in the boxes.

$2 + 3 + 5 =$ ☐

$2 + 2 + 2 =$ ☐

$6 + 1 + 3 =$ ☐

$4 + 1 + 6 =$ ☐

$7 + 2 + 3 =$ ☐

$0 + 5 + 0 =$ ☐

$4 + 3 + 4 =$ ☐

$1 + 10 + 10 =$ ☐

$9 + 3 + 3 =$ ☐

$10 + 10 + 10 =$ ☐

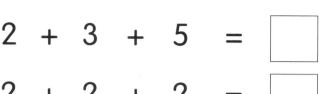

Number order

Write these sets of numbers in order.
Start with the lowest number.

7 2 4 1 3 6 5

_____

16 4 6 2 14 8 10 12

_____

53 33 3 0 30 13 23

_____

40 70 20 30 10 50 60

_____

Up, up and away

Draw lines to join pairs of numbers that total 20.

Flying high

Draw lines to join pairs of numbers that have a difference of 4.

Multiplication madness

The scientist has forgotten his times tables.
Help him by completing these sums.

5 times table

1 x 5 =
2 x 5 =
3 x 5 =
4 x 5 =
5 x 5 =
6 x 5 =
7 x 5 =

9 times table

1 x 9 =
2 x 9 =
3 x 9 =
4 x 9 =
5 x 9 =
6 x 9 =
7 x 9 =

10 times table

1 x 10 =
2 x 10 =
3 x 10 =
4 x 10 =
5 x 10 =
6 x 10 =
7 x 10 =

7 times table

1 x 7 =
2 x 7 =
3 x 7 =
4 x 7 =
5 x 7 =
6 x 7 =
7 x 7 =

8 times table

1 x 8 =
2 x 8 =
3 x 8 =
4 x 8 =
5 x 8 =
6 x 8 =
7 x 8 =

Skateboard sums

Draw lines to join the sums with their answers.

Multiplying by 10

By adding 0 to the end of a number, you multiply it by 10. Do these sums.

$1 \times 10 =$ ☐

$2 \times 10 =$ ☐

$3 \times 10 =$ ☐

$4 \times 10 =$ ☐

$5 \times 10 =$ ☐

$6 \times 10 =$ ☐

$7 \times 10 =$ ☐

$10 \times 10 =$ ☐

$100 \times 10 =$ ☐

$1000 \times 10 =$ ☐

Count with Dracula

Do the sums on Dracula's coffins.

3×2
4×9
$20 \div 5$
$12 - 6$
$5 + 4$
3×3
$7 - 2$

8×3
$5 - 5$
$15 \div 3$
6×2
$13 - 10$
$9 + 3$
$6 - 5$

$3 + 7$
$19 - 7$
1×8
$11 - 6$
$6 \div 2$
$7 - 3$
$8 + 2$

1×0
3×6
$10 \div 1$
5×4
$18 - 5$
$9 + 2$
$1 + 1$

Dividing

Draw lines to join the sums to their answers.

6 ÷ 2 =   12 ÷ 3 =

10 ÷ 2 =   12 ÷ 12 =

14 ÷ 2 =   20 ÷ 10 =

60 ÷ 6 =   6 ÷ 3 =

88 ÷ 8 =   24 ÷ 6 =

5 ÷ 1 =   14 ÷ 7 =

3	4	5	1
7	2	10	2
11	4	5	2

Dividing by 10

By removing 0 from the end of a number, you divide it by 10. Do these sums.

$10 \div 10 =$

$20 \div 10 =$

$30 \div 10 =$

$40 \div 10 =$

$50 \div 10 =$

$60 \div 10 =$

$70 \div 10 =$

$80 \div 10 =$

$90 \div 10 =$

$100 \div 10 =$

Double trouble

Double the numbers on these monster twins.

30

15

44

9

12

100

7

25

Half the bother

Halve the numbers on each of the sails.

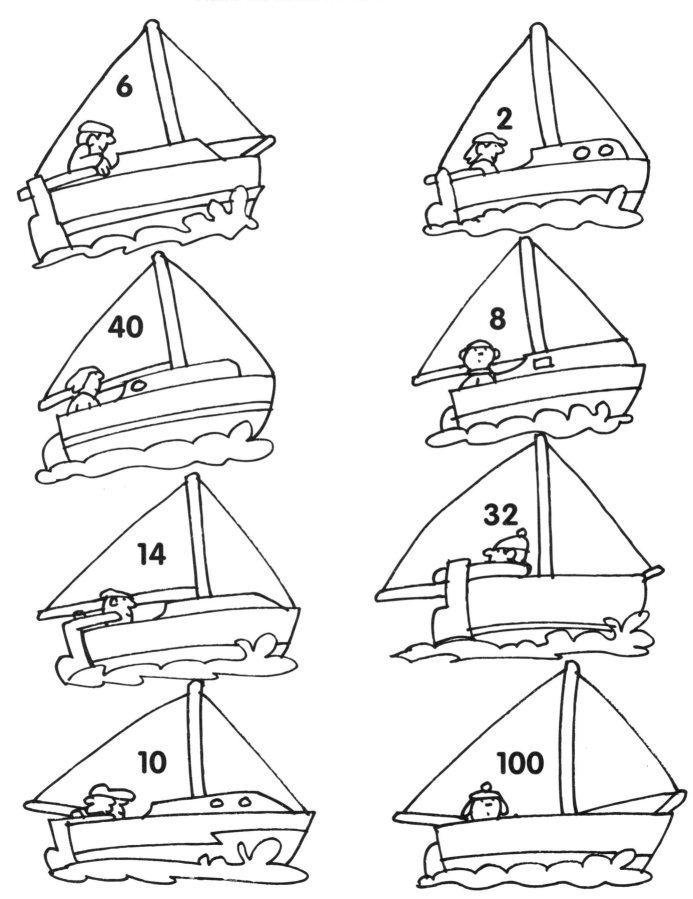

Shapes

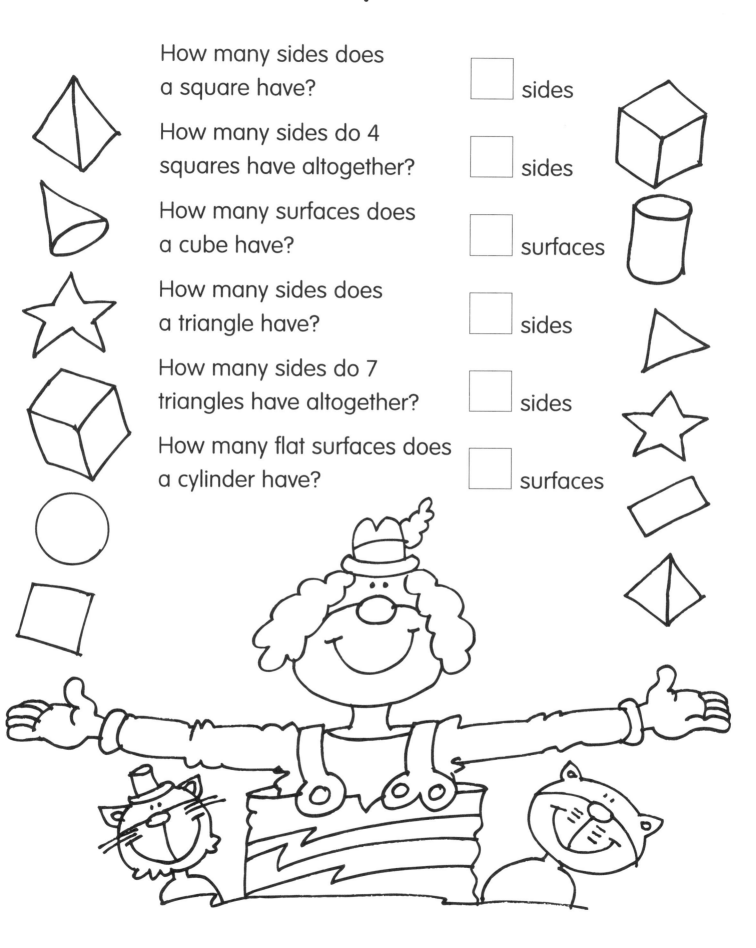

How many sides does a square have?

☐ sides

How many sides do 4 squares have altogether?

☐ sides

How many surfaces does a cube have?

☐ surfaces

How many sides does a triangle have?

☐ sides

How many sides do 7 triangles have altogether?

☐ sides

How many flat surfaces does a cylinder have?

☐ surfaces

Speed test 1

Answer these questions as quickly as you can.

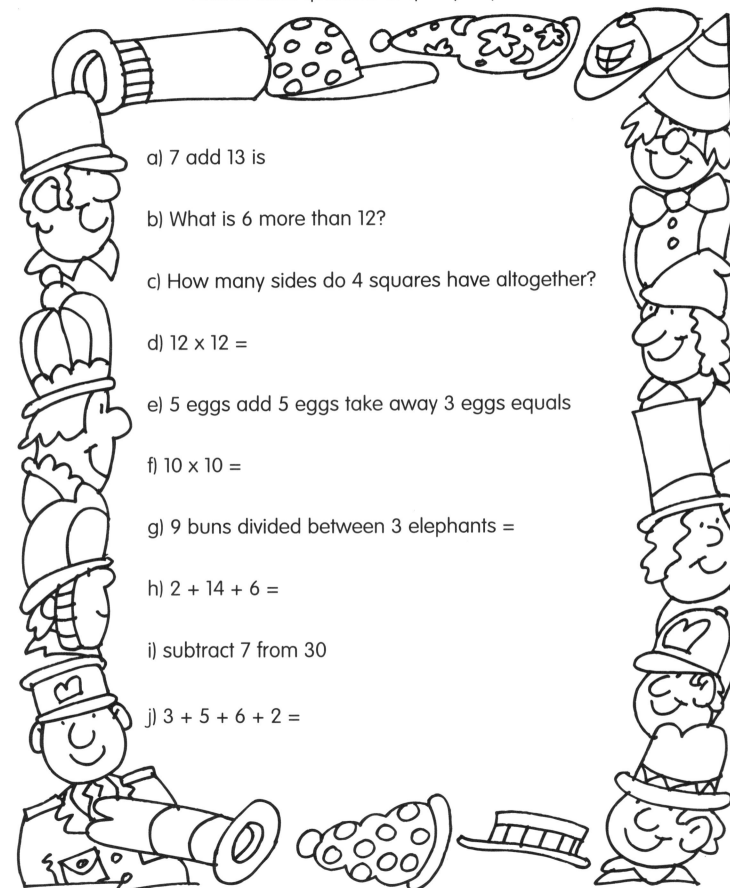

a) 7 add 13 is

b) What is 6 more than 12?

c) How many sides do 4 squares have altogether?

d) 12 x 12 =

e) 5 eggs add 5 eggs take away 3 eggs equals

f) 10 x 10 =

g) 9 buns divided between 3 elephants =

h) 2 + 14 + 6 =

i) subtract 7 from 30

j) 3 + 5 + 6 + 2 =

Speed test 2

Answer these questions as quickly as you can.

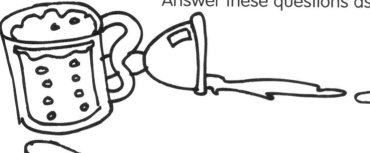

a) 100 ÷ 10 =

b) 2 x 2 x 2 =

c) add 20 to 15

d) There are 18 mice. The cat chases 6 mice.
   How many are left?

e) 17 is how many more than 10?

f) 3 + 5 + 15 =

g) 12 take away 7 equals

h) 19 add 5 is

i) 3 triangles have 6 sides altogether. True or false?

j) 13 + 4 + 4 =

Speed test 3

Answer these questions as quickly as you can.

a) 7 birds from 13 birds equals

b) 4 __ 12 __ 20 24 __ 32 __ 40

c) A rectangle has 6 sides. True or false?

d) 3 x 3 x 3 =

e) take 16 from 20

f) 10 x 10 =

g) If there are 14 fish in a net and 5 jump out,
   how many are left?

h) What is 8 more than 13?

i) 4 + 7 + 2 + 1 + 0 =

j) __ 90 __ 70 __ 50 __ 30 __ 10

Answers

Pet problems
4 + 3 = 7   6 + 4 = 10
2 + 4 = 6   1 + 1 = 2
2 + 1 = 3

Adding numbers
7 add 2 = 9   11 add 11 = 22
4 plus 4 = 8   9 plus 7 = 16
6 and 6 = 12   12 + 12 = 24
3 add 8 = 11   6 and 5 = 11
9 plus 4 = 13   eight plus two = 10
7 + 7 = 14   9 add 8 = 17
5 and 5 = 10   11 plus 12 = 23
10 + 11 = 21   4 and 8 = 12
8 + 7 = 15   one add six = 7
6 plus 8 = 14   5 + 10 = 15

Farmyard frolics
There are 19 sheep altogether.
Farmer Stan collects 8 hay bales altogether.
There are 11 eggs altogether.
There are 12 piglets altogether.

Pyramid puzzlers
11   15   14   22   12
7 4   10 5   11 3   11 11   6 6
4 3 1   7 3 2   9 2 1   6 5 6   3 3 3

Brain teasers
1 more than 5 is 6   11 more than 9 is 20
2 more than 3 is 5   8 more than 4 is 12
4 more than 6 is 10   3 more than 2 is 5
5 more than 5 is 10   10 more than 12 is 22
9 more than 3 is 12   4 more than 2 is 6
7 more than 7 is 14   9 more than 6 is 15

Fishing for 20
7 + 13   18 + 2   12 + 8   4 + 16
11 + 9   1 + 19   10 + 10

Seaside subtraction
7 - 2 = 5   6 - 3 = 3   10 - 9 = 1
5 - 5 = 0   9 - 3 = 6

Subtracting numbers
12 minus 5 = 7   11 take away 7 equals 4
15 minus 5 = 10   6 from 9 is 3
3 subtract 2 equals 1   14 - 7 = 7
19 from 20 = 1   10 take away 2 is 8

7 take away 4 is 3   5 from 20 is 15
12 - 5 = 7   nine minus three equals 6
20 minus 17 equals 3   4 subtract 2 is 2

Pond problems
6 ducks are left   8 dragonflies are left
6 frogs remain   8 snails remain

Baby blocks
0   3   15   4
4 4   4 1   17 2   10 6
11 7 3   12 8 7   20 3 1   18 8 2

10   4   2
10 0   10 6   4 2
20 10 10   19 9 3   15 11 9

Computer crazy

START	ADD		EQUALS		SUBTRACT		TOTAL
2	+	1	=	3	-	2	= 1
6	+	2	=	8	-	4	= 4
5	+	5	=	10	-	5	= 5
1	+	10	=	11	-	5	= 6
4	+	6	=	10	-	6	= 4

Number patterns
1 2 3 4 5 6 7   4 8 12 16 20 24 28
10 9 8 7 6 5 4   5 10 15 20 25 30 35
2 4 6 8 10 12 14   100 99 98 97 96 95 94
3 6 9 12 15 18 21   49 42 35 28 21 14 7

Number trails
2 + 3 + 5 = 10   0 + 5 + 0 = 5
2 + 2 + 2 = 6   4 + 3 + 4 = 11
6 + 1 + 3 = 10   1 + 10 + 10 = 21
4 + 1 + 6 = 11   9 + 3 + 3 = 15
7 + 2 + 3 = 12   10 + 10 + 10 = 30

Number order
1 2 3 4 5 6 7   0 3 13 23 30 33 53
2 4 6 8 10 12 14 16   10 20 30 40 50 60 70

Up, up and away
0 + 20 = 20   1 + 19 = 20   7 + 13 = 20
10 + 10 = 20   17 + 3 = 20   12 + 8 = 20

Flying high
1 and 5   30 and 34   6 and 10
8 and 12   44 and 48   20 and 24

Multiplication madness

1 x 5 = 5	1 x 9 = 9	1 x 10 = 10
2 x 5 = 10	2 x 9 = 18	2 x 10 = 20
3 x 5 = 15	3 x 9 = 27	3 x 10 = 30
4 x 5 = 20	4 x 9 = 36	4 x 10 = 40
5 x 5 = 25	5 x 9 = 45	5 x 10 = 50
6 x 5 = 30	6 x 9 = 54	6 x 10 = 60
7 x 5 = 35	7 x 9 = 63	7 x 10 = 70

1 x 7 = 7	1 x 8 = 8
2 x 7 = 14	2 x 8 = 16
3 x 7 = 21	3 x 8 = 24
4 x 7 = 28	4 x 8 = 32
5 x 7 = 35	5 x 8 = 40
6 x 7 = 42	6 x 8 = 48
7 x 7 = 49	7 x 8 = 56

Skateboard sums

65 - 5 = 60	21 + 12 = 33	8 x 8 = 64
60 ÷ 10 = 6	3 x 9 = 27	7 x 3 = 21
10 ÷ 2 = 5		

Multiplying by 10

1 x 10	=	10
2 x 10	=	20
3 x 10	=	30
4 x 10	=	40
5 x 10	=	50
6 x 10	=	60
7 x 10	=	70
10 x 10	=	100
100 x 10	=	1,000
1000 x 10	=	10,000

Count with Dracula

3 x 2 = 6	8 x 3 = 24
4 x 9 = 36	5 - 5 = 0
20 ÷ 5 = 4	15 ÷ 3 = 5
12 - 6 = 6	6 x 2 = 12
5 + 4 = 9	13 - 10 = 3
3 x 3 = 9	9 + 3 = 12
7 - 2 = 5	6 - 5 = 1

3 + 7 = 10	1 x 0 = 0
19 - 7 = 12	3 x 6 = 18
1 x 8 = 8	10 ÷ 1 = 10
11 - 6 = 5	5 x 4 = 20
6 ÷ 2 = 3	18 - 5 = 13
7 - 3 = 4	9 + 2 = 11
8 + 2 = 10	1 + 1 = 2

Dividing

6 ÷ 2 = 3	12 ÷ 3 = 4
10 ÷ 2 = 5	12 ÷ 12 = 1
14 ÷ 2 = 7	20 ÷ 10 = 2
60 ÷ 6 = 10	6 ÷ 3 = 2
88 ÷ 8 = 11	24 ÷ 6 = 4
5 ÷ 1 = 5	14 ÷ 7 = 2

Dividing by 10

10 ÷ 10	= 1
20 ÷ 10	= 2
30 ÷ 10	= 3
40 ÷ 10	= 4
50 ÷ 10	= 5
60 ÷ 10	= 6
70 ÷ 10	= 7
80 ÷ 10	= 8
90 ÷ 10	= 9
100 ÷ 10	= 10

Double trouble

30 - 60	15 - 30	44 - 88	9 - 18
12 - 24	100 - 200	7 - 14	25 - 50

Half the bother

6 - 3	2 - 1	40 - 20	8 - 4
14 - 7	32 - 16	10 - 5	100 - 50

Shapes

A square has 4 sides.
4 squares have 16 sides altogether.
A cube has 6 surfaces.
A triangle has 3 sides.
7 triangles have 21 sides.
A cylinder has 2 flat surfaces.

Speed test 1

a) 20	b)18	c) 16	d)144	e) 7
f) 100	g) 3	h) 22	i) 23	j) 16

Speed test 2

a) 10	b) 8	c) 35	d) 12	e) 7
f) 23	g) 5	h) 24	i) false	j) 21

Speed test 3

a) 6 birds	b) 8 16 28 36	c) false
d) 27	e) 4	f) 100
g) 9	h) 21	i) 14
j) 100 80 60 40 20		